W9-CKI-714

GARDEN
·GATES·

Grateful acknowledgment is made to the following publishers, authors, and agents for their permission to reprint copyrighted material. Any adaptations are noted in the individual acknowledgments and are made with the full knowledge and approval of the authors or their representatives. Every effort has been made to locate all copyright proprietors; any errors or omissions in copyright notice are inadvertent and will be corrected in future printings as they are discovered.

The Biggest Living Thing by Caroline Arnold. Copyright © 1983 by Carolrhoda Books, Inc. Adapted and reprinted by permission of Carolrhoda Books, Inc., 241 First Avenue North, Minneapolis, MN 55401.

The Caterpillar and the Polliwog written and illustrated by Jack Kent. Copyright © 1982 by Jack Kent. Adapted and used by permission of the publisher, Prentice-Hall, Inc., Englewood Cliffs, N. J.

Check It Out! written and illustrated by Gail Gibbons. Copyright © 1985 by Gail Gibbons. Adapted and reprinted by permission of Harcourt Brace Jovanovich, Inc.

Daniel's Duck by Clyde Robert Bulla. Text copyright © 1979 by Clyde Robert Bulla. Adapted and reprinted by permission of Harper & Row, Publishers, Inc., and of the author in care of his agents, Bill Berger Associates.

Frederick written and illustrated by Leo Lionni, adapted and reprinted by permission of Pantheon Books, a Division of Random House, Inc., and of Andersen Press. Copyright © 1967 by Leo Lionni.

Acknowledgments continue on pages 334–336, which constitute an extension of this copyright page.

© **1989 Silver, Burdett & Ginn Inc. All rights reserved.**
Printed in the United States of America. This publication, or parts thereof, may not be reproduced in any form by photographic, electrostatic, mechanical, or any other method, for any use, including information storage and retrieval, without written permission from the publisher.　　　ISBN 0-663-46115-4

WORLD OF READING

GARDEN ·GATES·

P. David Pearson   Dale D. Johnson

Theodore Clymer   Roselmina Indrisano   Richard L. Venezky

James F. Baumann   Elfrieda Hiebert   Marian Toth

Consulting Authors

Carl Grant   Jeanne Paratore

SILVER BURDETT & GINN

NEEDHAM, MA • MORRISTOWN, NJ
ATLANTA, GA • CINCINNATI, OH • DALLAS, TX
MENLO PARK, CA • NORTHFIELD, IL

HOUSE AND HOME — 84

UNIT
TWO

GIFTS AND TREASURES — 154

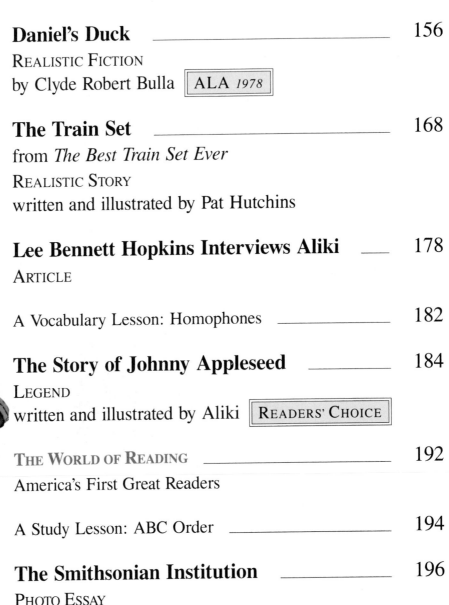

UNIT
THREE

UNIT FOUR

HERE'S THE PLAN — 222

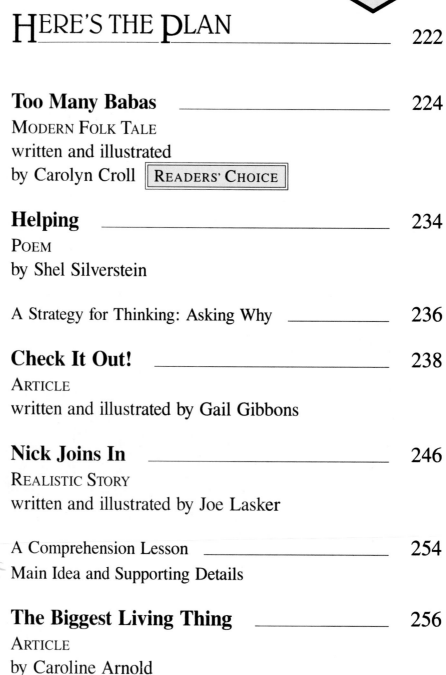

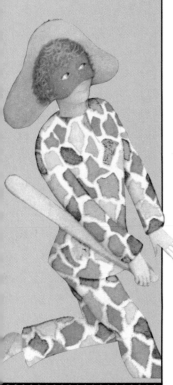

You
Can do it

*I*t sometimes takes courage to try something new.

Where does the courage come from?

GIRL WITH ROLLER SKATES,
*bronze sculpture by Abastenia St. Leger Eberle,
American, before 1909*

In this story Frog and Toad learn whether they are brave.

FROG
AND
TOAD

written and illustrated by Arnold Lobel
from
Frog and Toad Together

Frog and Toad were reading a book together. "The people in this book are brave," said Toad. "They fight dragons and giants, and they are never afraid."

NEWBERY
HONOR
1973

"I wonder if we are brave," said Frog. Frog
and Toad looked into a mirror.

"We look brave," said Frog.

"Yes, but are we?" asked Toad.

Frog and Toad went outside. "We can try to climb this mountain," said Frog. "That should tell us if we are brave."

Frog went leaping over rocks, and Toad came puffing up behind him. They came to a dark cave. A big snake came out of the cave.

"Hello lunch," said the snake when he saw
Frog and Toad. He opened his wide mouth.
Frog and Toad jumped away. Toad was shaking.

"I am not afraid!" he cried.

They climbed higher, and they heard a
loud noise. Many large stones were rolling
down the mountain.

"It's an avalanche!" cried Toad. Frog and
Toad jumped away. Frog was shaking.

"I am not afraid!" he shouted.

They came to the top of the mountain. The
shadow of a hawk fell over them. Frog and Toad
jumped under a rock. The hawk flew away.

"We are not afraid!" screamed Frog and
Toad at the same time. Then they ran down the
mountain very fast. They ran past the place
where they saw the avalanche. They ran past
the place where they saw the snake. They ran
all the way to Toad's house.

"Frog, I am glad to have a brave friend like you," said Toad. He jumped into the bed and pulled the covers over his head, still shaking.

"And I am happy to know a brave person like you, Toad," said Frog. He jumped into the closet and shut the door.

Toad stayed in the bed, and Frog stayed in the closet. They stayed there for a long time, just feeling very brave together.

◆ LIBRARY LINK ◆

Look for other books by Arnold Lobel in your library: Days with Frog and Toad, Frog and Toad All Year, *and* Frog and Toad Are Friends.

Reader's Response

Do you think Frog and Toad were brave? Tell why.

FROG AND TOAD

 ## Questions

1. Why did Toad think the people in the book were brave?
2. Why do you think Frog and Toad kept saying, "I am not afraid"?
3. What did Frog and Toad do after they reached Toad's house?
4. Do you think this story really happened? How do you know?

 ## Writing to Learn

THINK AND PREDICT Can you think of a new title for a story about Frog and Toad? Will they be brave?

WRITE Write two sentences that tell what Frog and Toad might do in a new story. Add a title.

The ugly duckling is lonely. Then,
something happens.

The Ugly Duckling

by Hans Christian Andersen
retold by Karen-Amanda Toulon

It was a beautiful day in the country.
The sun shone on the green grass, and birds
flew in the bright blue sky. The air was full
of summer.

There was an old farmhouse not far
from a pond. The grass near this pond was
soft and tall. It was in this lovely place that
a mother duck had made her nest.

It was time for the mother duck to hatch her ducklings. What a long job it was! She had sat on her eggs for days and days. At last, one began to crack and out came a little yellow duckling. The other eggs began to hatch, too, and soon there were many little ducklings.

"Oh, what a big world this is!" said the ducklings. Now they had much more room to move than when they were in the eggs.

"Do you think this is the world?" said
their mother. "Why, the world goes way past
this nest, right into that garden over there!
Now, let me see, are we all here?"

There was still one egg in the nest.
"How much longer can this take?" she said.
The mother duck sat down on the egg and
waited some more. At last she heard a loud
CRACK. A big gray duckling came out of the
shell. It was very large and very ugly.

The ugly duckling looked at the mother duck and said, "Peep, peep, peep."

"You don't look like one of my ducklings," said the mother. "You are too big and gray." The ugly duckling made a sad peep.

"Well," said the mother, "we will see about you. All ducks can swim. Let us see if you can." With that, the mother duck took all the ducklings down to the pond.

"You must be my duckling," said the proud mother to the ugly duckling. "Why, look how well you swim. Come. Let me show you to my friends," she said and took her ducklings to meet the other ducks.

The other ducks were not at all kind to the ugly duckling. "What a strange duckling!" they said. "Send him away! He is too ugly to be with us."

The ducks picked on the ugly duckling to no end. They bit his neck and legs. As time went on, things did not get any better. The duckling felt so ugly and alone that he ran away.

The sad, little ugly duckling went very far. Night came. He saw a house. The door was open a bit, so he went in.

A woman lived in the house with her cat and her hen. When she saw the ugly duckling, she thought he could lay eggs like a hen.

"Now I will have duck eggs," said the woman. She let the ugly duckling stay.

The cat and the hen were very hard to live with. They picked on the ugly duckling all of the time because he could not lay eggs like a hen or climb like a cat. Once again, the ugly duckling felt sad and alone.

One day the ugly duckling thought of how he missed the country. He thought of the bright sun and the lovely green grass. But more than anything, he wanted to be in the pond. He wanted to swim and feel the water all around him. He told the cat and the hen about it.

"How silly you are, you poor, ugly duckling," they said. "No one who is anything would want to be in water."

"You don't understand," said the
ugly duckling.

"Be quiet," said the cat, "and be glad
that you have friends who can tell you what
is right. Just see to it that you lay some eggs
soon." The ugly duckling knew it was time
to leave the woman's house, so off he went.

Fall came. The leaves turned red and
yellow. Soon they fell off the trees and
began to blow about. The wind grew
stronger and stronger. The air grew colder
and colder.

One day the ugly duckling saw some big birds fly out from behind some trees. He had never seen such beautiful birds. They were white, with long, lovely necks and strong wings.

The ugly duckling watched them fly higher and higher into the air. He felt very strange. He didn't know what the birds were called or where they were going, but he felt so close to them in his heart. He wanted to be with them. As they flew away, the ugly duckling let out a sad cry. He would always remember those beautiful birds.

Winter came. It grew very, very cold.
The duckling had to keep moving through
the wind and the snow and the ice, so he
would not freeze.

It would be too sad to tell all of the hard
times the ugly duckling had that winter. Let
us just say that the sun began to get warm
again, and spring came at last.

One warm spring day, the duckling flew
up into the air. His wings felt very strong.
He had never gone so high or so fast. He felt
proud. Soon he was flying over a lovely
garden with a pond. In the pond were those
beautiful, white birds he had seen before.
When the ugly duckling saw them, he got
that same strange feeling again.

"I must be near them," he thought. "I
know they will not talk to me because I am
so ugly. But I must go to them. They are
so beautiful." And then he flew down to
the pond.

The ugly duckling swam near the beautiful, white birds. They saw him and swam close to him. The poor duckling put his head down in shame because he thought he looked so ugly. But when he looked down, what did he see in the water? He saw a beautiful, white bird, not an ugly duckling. He was just like the others. He could not believe it was true.

Two children were playing in the garden. They called out with joy, "Look! Look at the new swan. He is the most beautiful swan of all."

Then three great swans came to the new
swan and stroked him with their beaks.
They, too, thought he was beautiful. He was
proud and full of joy, for he had friends at
last.

◆ LIBRARY LINK ◆

*Hans Christian Andersen has written
many stories for children. One story you
may enjoy is called* The Nightingale.

Reader's Response

Would you be a friend to the ugly
duckling? Tell why or why not.

The Ugly Duckling

Questions

1. How was the ugly duckling different from the other ducklings?
2. How did the other ducks treat the ugly duckling? How did you decide on your answer?
3. What happened to change the duckling's feelings about himself?

Writing to Learn

THINK AND DECIDE Did you feel sorry for the ugly duckling? Were you happy when he found his swan family? Draw a picture of the ugly duckling from a part of the story you like.

My picture of the Ugly Duckling

WRITE Look at your picture. Write one sentence that tells about your picture.

Art That Wins the Gold

▲ The Caldecott Medal

Close your eyes. Think about your favorite book. What do you see? Pictures! Words tell stories, but often it is the pictures that make a book one you always remember.

Maybe you have seen the gold Caldecott Medal on the cover of one of your favorite books. It is a special prize that is given every year to the person who draws the best pictures for a children's book.

▲ *Arrow to the Sun*

Where the Wild Things Are ▶

WHERE THE WILD THINGS ARE

STORY AND PICTURES BY MAURICE SENDAK

The medal is on the cover of *Where the Wild Things Are* by Maurice Sendak. Have you read this book?

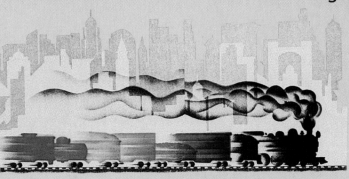

▲ *Ben's Trumpet*

Rachael Isadora won the Caldecott Medal for her drawings in *Ben's Trumpet*. She also drew the pictures for our next story, *Max*.

Donald Crews had two Caldecott Honor Books, *Freight Train* and *Truck*.

Gerald McDermott used desert colors, brown and yellow and red, in his pictures of Pueblo Indians. His book *Arrow to the Sun* won a Caldecott Medal, too.

The next time you go to the library, see if you can find a Caldecott Medal book. Your librarian can help you choose one to take home.

◀ Donald Crews

▼ *Freight Train*

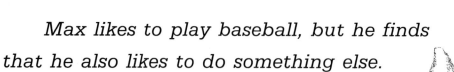

*Max likes to play baseball, but he finds
that he also likes to do something else.*

written and illustrated
by Rachel Isadora

MAX

AMERICAN
LIBRARY
ASSOCIATION
1976

Max is a great baseball player. He can run fast, jump high, and he hardly ever misses a catch.

Every Saturday he plays baseball with his team in the park. On Saturday mornings he walks with his sister Lisa to her dancing school. The school is on the way to the park.

One Saturday when they reach the dancing school, Max still has lots of time before the game is to start. Lisa asks him if he wants to come inside for a while. Max doesn't really want to, but he says OK.

Soon the class begins. Max gets a chair and sits near the door to watch.

The teacher asks Max to dance with the class, but he must take off his sneakers first.

He stretches at the *barre* (bär).

He tries to do the split.

And then he tries the *pas de chat* (pä-də-shä'). He is having fun.

Just as the class lines up to do leaps, his sister points to the clock. It is time for Max to leave. Max doesn't want to miss the leaps. He waits and takes his turn. Then he must go.

He is late. Everyone is waiting for him.

He goes up to bat. Strike one! He tries again. Strike two! And then . . .

A HOME RUN!

Now Max has a new way to warm up
for the baseball game on Saturdays. He
goes to dancing class with his sister. He
leaps all the way to the park.

Reader's Response

Would you like Max to be your
brother? Tell why or why not.

◆ Questions

1. Why was Max a great baseball player?
2. How are dancing and baseball alike? How are they different?
3. Why did Max have so much fun dancing?
4. How did dancing school help Max with baseball? How do you know?
5. Were you surprised that Max liked to dance? Tell why or why not.

◆ Writing to Learn

THINK AND COMPARE   This story is about Max and his sister. Max likes to dance and play baseball. His sister likes to dance. Draw a picture of yourself. Show something that you like to do.

WRITE   Look at your picture. Write two sentences that tell what you are doing in your picture.

Vocabulary:

Multiple Meanings

In the story, "Max," Max was a great baseball player. He could run fast, jump high, and hit home runs with his baseball bat.

Some words, like *bat,* can have more than one meaning. Read these sentences. Look at the word *bat* in each sentence.

1. Max loved baseball, so his parents gave him a new *bat.*
2. The black *bat* flew over our house.

In sentence 1, the word *bat* means "a club or stick used to hit a baseball." In sentence 2, the word *bat* means "an animal that flies."

You can figure out words that have more than one meaning if you look at the other words in the sentence.

Read the sentences on the next page. Think about the meaning of the word *park* in each sentence.

1. Max plays ball in the *park*.
2. His mother will *park* the car.

In sentence 1, the word *park* means "place where people come to rest and to play." The words *plays ball* gave you a clue.

In sentence 2, the word *park* means "leave the car in a certain place." Which word gave you a clue?

Using What You Have Learned

What does the word *points* mean in this sentence?

Lisa points to the clock on the wall.

Can you think of another meaning for the word *points*? Use the other meaning in a sentence.

As You Read

In the next story, "The Skating Lesson," find an important word that has more than one meaning.

The Skating Lesson

by Johanna Hurwitz

When you learn something new, grown-ups often help. But it doesn't always work that way.

Since November, Makiko Ogawa (mu-kē'-kō ō-gä'-wu) had gone ice-skating every Saturday. She always went with her friend Carmen and Carmen's brother, Luis (lo͞o-ēs'). Luis was old enough to take the two girls skating in the park.

Makiko didn't have her own ice skates, so Luis lent her his old black skates. Makiko had to put on two pairs of socks so they would fit, but the skates worked well enough. She wished that she would get a pair of girl's white skates, like Carmen's, for her birthday.

The first time Makiko went skating she was scared. She thought she would fall. Luis taught her to look ahead, not down at her feet. When she looked ahead, she forgot she was wearing his old skates. Makiko loved to feel herself glide smoothly along on the ice.

Makiko went skating all winter. Each time she used Luis's old skates, she wished for a pair of her own.

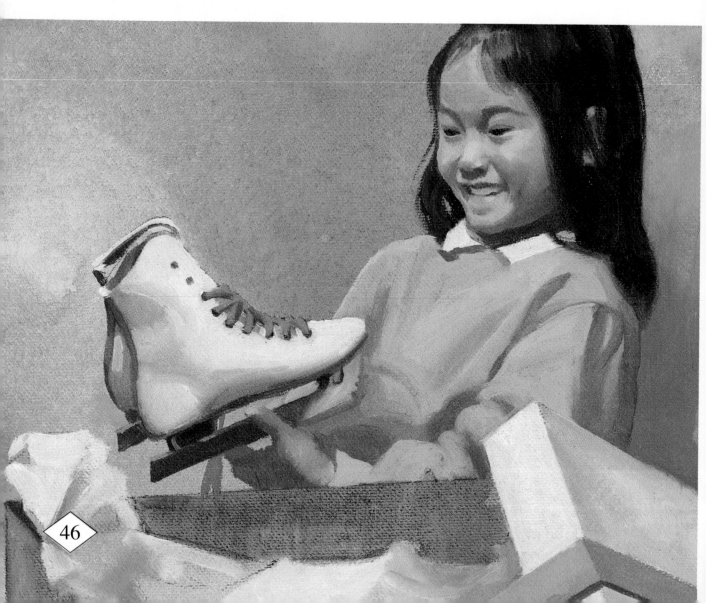

When Makiko's birthday came, there was a big box waiting for her. Makiko was afraid to look inside. Maybe it would not be what she really wanted.

Makiko slowly opened the box. Inside was a pair of white ice skates! They were just like Carmen's. Makiko gave her mother and father a big hug. She was very, very happy with her new skates. She couldn't wait to try them out.

The sun was bright and the air cold the next Saturday. There was no wind. It was a great day for skating, until Carmen called Makiko that morning.

"Luis and I can't go skating today," Carmen said. "Our grandmother is coming over. We want to stay here and visit with her."

Makiko was very upset. When Mrs. Ogawa saw how Makiko felt, she told Makiko she would take her skating. "I know how much you want to try your birthday skates," her mother said. Makiko gave her mother a hug. Then Makiko ran and got her skates.

Many people were skating. Makiko rushed to put on her skates. She couldn't wait to get on the ice.

"Watch me," she called to her mother as she skated away. At first the new skates felt a little stiff and strange, but soon Makiko was skating smoothly. She waved to her mother. Mrs. Ogawa waved back. Makiko skated around and around. The next time Makiko saw her mother, she looked blue with cold. Makiko skated to the fence.

"We can't stay too much longer," said Mrs.
Ogawa. "I am so cold. I feel like I'm turning
to ice."

"Skate with me, and you won't be so
cold," Makiko said. "Skating keeps
you warm."

"I can't skate," said Mrs. Ogawa.
"Skating is for children."

"No, it isn't," said Makiko. "Look."
She pointed to a man and woman who were
skating past.

"I don't have any ice skates, Makiko," said Mrs. Ogawa.

"You can rent a pair," said Makiko. "A lot of people here are wearing rented skates. If Luis had not let me use his old skates, I would have rented them."

"Even if adults can skate and even if I rented skates, I still can't skate," said Mrs. Ogawa. "I don't know how."

Makiko had never thought of that. She thought her mother knew everything. "I could teach you," she said. "Luis taught me. Now I can teach you. It isn't hard."

"But the ice is very hard," said Makiko's mother, looking a little afraid.

"You won't fall. You can skate slowly, near the fence, and hold on when you need to," Makiko said. "I'll be right here."

Mrs. Ogawa thought about it. "Why not?" she said. "It does look like fun."

Soon Mrs. Ogawa was wearing a pair of skates for the first time. She walked slowly onto the ice, holding onto the fence as she moved. She was a bit shaky.

"Now, the first thing is to look ahead, not at your feet," Makiko said, thinking back to her first lesson with Luis. Very slowly the two of them moved together on the ice. Mrs. Ogawa took little steps, as if she were walking on the ice.

"Try not to walk when you skate," said Makiko. "Let your feet glide, one at a time. You want to move smoothly."

"I'm afraid," said Mrs. Ogawa, laughing at herself.

"I won't let you fall," Makiko said.
"Watch me." Makiko had never felt so big.

Then Makiko skated past her mother and showed her how to look ahead and make her feet glide over the ice. "Now you try," she said, skating back to hold her mother's hand.

"I can't believe I'm doing this," laughed Mrs. Ogawa.

"You're doing great!" said Makiko. "Do you want ice skates for your birthday, too?"

They skated until it was time to go home for lunch. "Thank you for teaching me to skate," said Mrs. Ogawa. "It was a lot of fun. I'm glad I didn't fall, and I stayed warm, too."

"I never knew I could be a teacher," said Makiko. "It was fun." She thought of how many things her mother had taught her.

"Will you come skating with me next week, too?" asked Makiko.

"I think it's good for you to be with your friends," said her mother, "but how about this? Some night we will ask your father to come with us. You can teach him how to ice-skate, too. It must be beautiful skating under the stars."

As Mrs. Ogawa took back her rented skates, Makiko, deep in thought, watched the people skating. Today she was proud of many things. She was proud of her new skates, and she was proud of her skating. Most of all, she was proud of teaching her mother how to do something new. Makiko smiled a big smile and then ran to meet her mother.

◆ LIBRARY LINK ◆

Look in the library for other books by Johanna Hurwitz, such as DeDe Takes Charge! *and* What Goes up Must Come down.

Reader's Response

Do you think Makiko was a good teacher? Tell why you think this.

The Skating Lesson

 ## Questions

1. Did Makiko like the idea of wearing Luis's skates? How do you know?
2. Why was Makiko upset the Saturday after she got her new skates?
3. Why did Makiko's mother want to learn to skate?
4. If Makiko had not taught her mother to skate, what might have happened?

 ## Writing to Learn

THINK AND DESCRIBE Would you be a good teacher? Do you like to play a game? Do you like to fly a kite? Could you tell a grown-up how to do it?

WRITE Choose one thing you would teach a grown-up. Write how to do it.

Thinking

by Felice Holman

Silently
Inside my head
Behind my eyes
A thought begins to grow and be
A part of me.
And then I think
I always knew
The thing I only got to know,
As though it always
Was right there
Inside my head
Behind my eyes
Where I keep things.

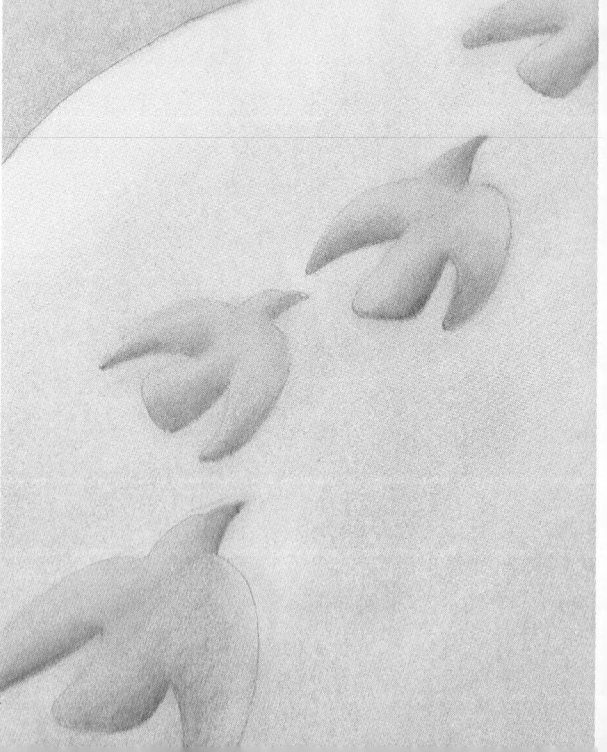

READING FICTION

Comprehension:
Making Inferences

In "Frog and Toad," the writer sometimes did not explain everything that happened in the story. Read the following sentences from "Frog and Toad."

A big snake came out of the cave. "Hello, lunch," said the snake when he saw Frog and Toad. He opened his wide mouth. Frog and Toad jumped away. Toad was shaking.

The writer did not tell you why Frog and Toad jumped away. But you can figure out why. You can use word clues from the story and think about what you already know about snakes. Frog and Toad jumped away because they were afraid of the snake. What clues help you know that?

Now read this paragraph about "The Ugly Duckling."

The sun shone on the green grass, and birds flew in the bright, blue sky. The old farmhouse stood not far from a pond. The grass near the pond was soft and tall. It was a lovely place for a mother duck to make a nest.

Where is the pond? Which words helped you know that the pond is in the country?

Using What You Have Learned

Read the paragraph. Answer the questions.

Makiko glided on the ice. She looked ahead, not down at her feet. The warm sun and cold air felt good. She didn't fall down once!

1. What season was it?
2. What was Makiko doing on the ice? What word clues helped you decide?
3. How was Makiko feeling? What clues helped you?

As You Read

The next story you will read is "Keep the Lights Burning, Abbie." Look for clues that help you figure out how Abbie is feeling.

READERS'
CHOICE
AWARD

Keep the Lights Burning, Abbie

written by Peter and Connie Roop

illustrated by Peter E. Hanson

This story tells how a young girl named Abbie Burgess tried to do her father's job.

Abbie looked out the lighthouse window. Waves washed up on the rocks. Out at sea, a ship sailed safely by.

"Will you sail to town today, Papa?" Abbie asked.

"Yes," said Captain Burgess. "Mama needs medicine. The lights need oil. We need food. The sea is quiet now. So it's safe to go out in my boat."

"But what if you don't get back today?" asked Abbie. "Who will take care of the lights?"

Papa smiled. "You will, Abbie."

"Oh, no, Papa!" said Abbie. "I have never done it alone."

"You have trimmed the wicks before," said Papa. "You have cleaned the lamps and put in the oil. Mama is too sick to do it. Your sisters are too little. You must keep the lights burning, Abbie. Many ships count on our lighthouses."

Abbie and Papa walked down to the sea. Their little boat pulled on its rope. Captain Burgess jumped into the boat and moved away, out to sea.

"Keep the lights burning, Abbie!" her father called.

"I will, Papa," Abbie cried. But the wind carried off her words.

Abbie watched her father sail out to sea. Far away, she could see Matinicus Island. She knew Papa could sail well. He could sail in rain. He could sail in fog. But if the wind blew up again, he could not sail back to Matinicus Rock today. The waves would be too high for the little boat. Then she would have to care for the lights.

Abbie looked up. The two lighthouses
seemed as high as the sky. Her family's stone
house sat between them. Not far away was
Abbie's henhouse.

Abbie went to see her hens. She sat on a
rock and watched them.

"I hope he gets home today," Abbie said to herself. "I am a little afraid to care for the lights alone."

Abbie walked to the house. Esther opened the door. "When is Papa coming back?" she asked.

"This afternoon," said Abbie.

"What if another storm starts?" asked her sister Mahala.

"Don't be afraid," Abbie told her. "Papa will come back as soon as he can."

"How is Mama?" Abbie asked her sister Lydia.

"Still too sick to get up," said Lydia. "It's a good thing Papa went today. Mama needs medicine. And we need more food."

"Then we must take care," said Abbie. "If there is another storm, Papa might not get back today. We must make the food last."

Outside, the sky turned gray. Another winter storm was coming.

When the sun went down, Abbie put on her coat. She had to light the lamps. Abbie ran up the lighthouse steps. At the top she looked out the window. The waves were like mountains. The wind blew rain at the windows. She could not even see Matinicus Island. She knew Papa could not sail back. Abbie was afraid. What if she could not light the lamps?

She picked up a box of matches. She was so afraid. Her hands were shaking. She lit a match, but it went out. She lit another. This one burned.

Abbie held the match near the wick of the
first lamp. The wick gave off a bright light.
The light made Abbie feel better. One by one,
she lit all the lamps. Then she went to the other
lighthouse. She lit those lamps as well.

Out at sea, a ship saw the lights. It turned
away from the rocks.

That night, the wind blew hard. Abbie
could not sleep. She kept thinking about the
lights. What if they went out? A ship might
crash.

Abbie got out of bed. She put on her coat. She climbed the lighthouse steps. It was a good thing she had come. There was ice on the windows. The lights could not be seen.

All night long, Abbie climbed up and down. She scraped ice off the windows. She checked each light. Not one went out.

In the morning, Abbie blew out each light. She trimmed each wick. She cleaned each lamp. She put in more oil. Then, at last, she went to bed.

For over a week, the wind and rain roared. One morning, water ran under the door.

''My hens!'' Abbie cried. ''They will be washed away.''

''Don't go outside,'' said Lydia. ''You'll be washed away, too.''

Abbie picked up a basket. ''I go outside every night,'' she said. ''I will not be washed away!''

She opened the door. Water splashed into the room. Abbie ran out into the rain. She ran through the water to the henhouse. She put one hen under her arm and pushed the other two into the basket. Just then she heard another big wave come roaring in.

Abbie ran as fast as she could back to the lighthouse. "Open the door!" she cried. Lydia opened the door. Abbie ran inside.

"Oh, look!" Mahala cried. "Look there! The sea is coming!"

The wave crashed over Matinicus Rock. It washed away the henhouse. The girls pushed the door shut. Then the wave hit it. Abbie felt the lighthouse shake. She was shaking, too. They had shut the door just in time.

Day after day, it snowed or rained. Abbie wished it would stop. She was tired of the wind. She was tired of the waves. She was tired of climbing the lighthouse steps.

Then one morning, the waves seemed smaller. The sky was not so black. The wind did not blow so hard.

Late that afternoon, the girls heard someone outside. It was Papa. They ran to help him with the boxes. There was medicine for Mama. There was oil for the lamps, and there was food.

"I was afraid for you," said Papa. "Every night I watched for the lights. Every night I saw them. Then I knew you were all right."

Abbie smiled.

"I kept the lights burning, Papa."

 Reader's Response

Would you like to have been Abbie? Why or why not?

Keep the Lights Burning, Abbie

Questions

1. Why was Abbie afraid to take care of the lights?
2. How did Abbie's father know that Abbie was all right?
3. What problems did Abbie face in taking care of the lights?
4. If Abbie had not kept the lights burning, what might have happened? What makes you think so?

Writing to Learn

THINK AND DESCRIBE What did you learn about Abbie? Read these sentence beginnings.

> Abbie is afraid because _____.
> Abbie is brave because _____.
> Abbie is careful because _____.

WRITE On your paper copy and finish the sentences about Abbie.

71

*As you grow,
you change. Polliwog
changes, too—and in
some special ways.*

The Caterpillar and the Polliwog

written
and
illustrated
by Jack Kent

Down by the pond there lived a
caterpillar who was very proud of being
different. She bragged about it to her
friends. "When I grow up, I'm going to turn
into something else," she told the snail.

"That's nice," said the snail, who really
didn't care one way or the other.

"When I grow up, I'm going to turn into
something else," she told the turtle.

"I don't blame you," said the turtle, who
didn't much like wiggly things.

"When I grow up, I'm going to turn into
something else," she told the polliwog.

"What fun!" said the polliwog. "What are
you going to turn into?" But the caterpillar
rushed away, looking for someone else to tell
her secret to.

"I wish *I* could turn into something else when I grow up!" said the polliwog.

"You *will*," said the fish.
"*All* polliwogs do."

"What am I going to turn into?" the polliwog asked. But the fish saw a tasty bug and dashed after it.

"When I grow up," said the caterpillar, who had circled the pond and was going around for the second time, "when I grow up," she told the polliwog again, "I'm going to turn into something else."

"So am *I*!" said the polliwog.

"*You*?!" The caterpillar was so surprised she almost fell into the pond.

"The fish said so," the polliwog told her. "Fish know things. They go to school."

The caterpillar was upset. "I thought only caterpillars could do it," she said rather sadly.

"What are we going to turn into?" the polliwog asked.

"Well, *I'm* going to turn into a *butterfly*!" said the caterpillar.

"Then I guess I will, too!" the polliwog said happily. "What fun! Let's do it together!"

"All right," said the caterpillar, although she would rather have done it alone. "But I get to go first!"

The polliwog didn't mind. He wasn't at all sure how it was done. "I'll watch you," he said.

So when the time came, the caterpillar started to spin a cocoon. "This is the tricky part," she said.

The polliwog watched as the caterpillar spun. Soon only her head showed.

"Now I have to close the lid," she said. "And when I come out, I'll be a butterfly."

"Go ahead!" the polliwog said excitedly. "I want to see you do it!"

"It will take a while," the caterpillar said. She started spinning again and was soon out of sight in the cocoon.

For a long time nothing
happened. But the polliwog
watched
and watched
and watched,
for days
and days
and days.

77

At last the cocoon started to move. The end of it opened and, very slowly, the caterpillar climbed out. Only she wasn't a caterpillar anymore. She was a *butterfly*! A beautiful yellow butterfly.

The polliwog was so excited he hopped up and down! He *hopped*! Up and down! Like a *frog*!

"I was so busy watching *you*," he said, "I didn't see what was happening to *me*!"

"You're a very handsome frog," the butterfly said, as she flew off to try her new wings.

But the frog was puzzled. "I thought I was going to be a butterfly," he said.

A caterpillar wiggled by. "When I grow up," he said proudly to the frog, "I'm going to turn into something else!"

But the frog wasn't listening. He was looking at himself in the water. "I *am*, you know, a *very* handsome frog!" he said.

 Reader's Response

Which character from the story did you like best? Tell why.

Writing About Learning Something

Think about the characters in the stories you have read. What did they learn?

Abbie learned that she could do a grown-up job. Makiko learned that she could teach her mother to skate.

You can write a paragraph about something you would like to learn, too.

Prewriting

Think of something you would like to learn to do. Would you like to learn to cook, skate, or draw?

Draw a picture that shows you doing the thing you want to learn.

Writing

Look at your picture. Then write a paragraph about what you learned to do. Explain why you learned it. Tell how you learned it.

Revising

Read what you wrote. Do you want to add another reason for learning something new?

Proofreading

Check your paper again. Does each sentence begin with a capital letter? Does each sentence end with a period?

On a clean sheet of paper, make a neat copy of what you have written.

Publishing

Print your name on your picture and on your paper. Then make a *New Things We Want to Learn* book with your class. Add your picture and your final copy.

Writing a Telegram

Today, your group will write a telegram. This is a telegram that was sent to Frog.

GOOD FOR YOU
WE KNEW YOU COULD DO IT!

Many characters in this unit did something well. Today you and your group will write a telegram to one of the characters.

Here are some things you can do as you work together:

♦ Encourage everyone to share ideas.

♦ Write down the names of story characters.

♦ Write what those characters did.

As a group, remember the story characters in this unit. Write their names. Talk about what each one did. Then, choose one to receive your telegram.

Talk about some messages your group could send. Then work together to write a telegram. Read your telegram to the members of another group.

Petunia by Roger Duvoisin *(Knopf, 1950)* This goose thinks *carrying* a book will make her wise, but soon she learns that wisdom comes from *reading* the book.

The Mixed-Up Chameleon by Eric Carle *(Crowell, 1984)* A chameleon tries to be other animals, but decides it's best to be itself.

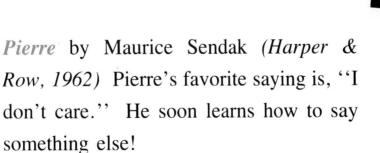

Say Hello, Vanessa by Marjorie Weinman Sharmat *(Holiday House, 1979)* Vanessa Mouse wants to have friends, but she is too shy to say hello.

Pierre by Maurice Sendak *(Harper & Row, 1962)* Pierre's favorite saying is, ''I don't care.'' He soon learns how to say something else!

UNIT TWO

HOUSE AND HOME

Feeling at home is a good feeling.

What makes people feel at home?

A TRAMP ON CHRISTMAS DAY,
painting by Grandma Moses, American, c. 1936

Some people have special feelings about their homes. A house can be more than just a building.

My HOUSE

by Miriam Schlein

There are a lot of houses where I live. One of them is MY HOUSE. That's the most important one—to me.

It is not the biggest house or the newest house. Some other houses have bigger trees in front, and they have more flowers growing in their gardens. But this one is MY HOUSE. It is special.

My house is where I come home when I have been away. It is where my bed is, and all my things, and the people that I love best. My house is where my books are, my shells, my little brother, my father and mother.

Before we moved in, my house was very much like any other house. But after we moved in, it became special.

My father put up shelves for *our* things. We painted the closets and hung our own clothes in them. We painted the rooms colors that *we* like. We hung up pictures and things that *we* like to look at. All these things helped make it *our* house.

It was spring when we moved in. We planted grass seed, and the grass grew. It's nice to sit on. There was a flower garden outside. We weeded and watered it. We cut some flowers and put them in the house. The flowers made things cheery. They made the house smell nice.

When a house is your house, you get to know it like a friend. You understand things about it that other people don't.

There is a scratching noise when the wind blows. It's nothing scary. "Oh," you say. "That noise is the branch of the dogwood tree, brushing against the window."

There is a whistling noise. You know what that is, too. "Oh," you say. "That is just the wind blowing down into the chimney."

A house grows with you. It grows older with you, and sometimes it grows bigger. Sometimes your family gets bigger, and you need more rooms in the house. So the rooms are added on.

A house has to be fixed up and taken care of, too—inside and out. There is a lot of work to do.

Sometimes I look at my house and I think of all the things that happened there. There was the time I had my birthday party. Then there was the time Dad fell down and hurt his leg. And there was the time Mom dropped the spaghetti! I think of all the times my dad sat by the window and read to me.

I think of all the cold mornings when I would stick just my feet out from under the covers, and Mom would put my socks on for me—so I could stay warm for a little bit longer. My house is where very special things happen —things that I remember.

My house is where my friends can come to see me. It is where people call me up. It is where I get my mail. And when I have gone out, no matter where I have been, it is the place I am always happy to come home to. My House.

◆ LIBRARY LINK ◆

It is fun to read about different kinds of houses. Look in the library for a book called A House is a House for Me *by Mary Ann Hoberman.*

Reader's Response

What was your favorite part of "My House"? Why was it your favorite?

My HOUSE

Questions

1. How did the girl feel when she came home?
2. What did the family do to the house to make it special?
3. How is a house like a person?
4. Is the house in this story in the city or in the country? What makes you think this?
5. Could the house in this story be a real house? How do you know?

Writing to Learn

THINK AND DESCRIBE Think of a house. What is your favorite place in that house? Draw a picture of it. Label your favorite things in the picture.

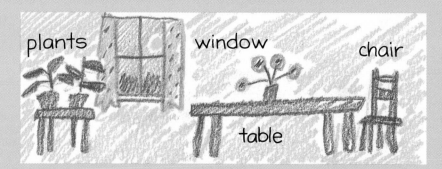

WRITE Look at your picture. Read the labels. Write why you like to be in your favorite place.

A Strategy for Thinking:

Making Pictures in Your Mind

How can you remember more of what you read? One way is to make pictures in your mind.

Learning the Strategy

When you read, try to make a picture in your mind of what the story tells you. If a boy hits a home run, try to picture him going around the bases.

Using the Strategy

You have read the story "My House." What did the girl's house look like? What did she say about her house? What special things did she have?

Read part of "My House" below. Make pictures in your mind of what you read.

My house is where I come home when I have been away. It is where my bed is, and all my things, and the people that I love best. My house is where my books are, my shells, my little brother, my father and mother.

Now close your eyes. What things in the house do you see?

Write a sentence about one of the things you remember.

Did making pictures in your mind help you remember?

Applying the Strategy to the Next Story

The next story that you will read is called "Not So Wise as You Suppose." At several points you will have a chance to make pictures in your mind. This will help you remember the story.

❖ The writing connection can be found on page 129.

*A farmer makes some changes at home.
But he is in for a big surprise!*

Not So Wise As You Suppose

by Michael Patrick Hearn

Once there was a farmer who went to the town wise man because he had a problem, and he did not know what to do. "How can I help you?" the wise man asked.

"I have a house with one small room," sighed the farmer.

"That is not a problem," the wise man said.

"It is a problem," the farmer sighed. "I live in this one small room with my wife and my seven children. We are always in one another's way, and we are always talking at the same time. It is so loud that I can hardly hear myself think. I cannot stand it any longer. Can you help me?"

95

The wise man stroked his chin and thought. "Do you have a horse?" the wise man asked.

"Yes, I have a horse," the farmer said.

"Then the answer is simple," the wise man said, "but you must do as I tell you. Tonight you must bring the horse into your house to stay with you, your wife, and your seven children." The farmer was surprised to hear such a plan, but he did as he was told.

The next morning he returned to the wise man. He was quite upset.

"You are not so wise as you suppose!" the farmer said. "Now my house is even louder. The horse just kicks and neighs morning, noon, and night! I cannot stand it any longer." ◄❖►

◄❖►
Can you picture the horse in your mind?

96

The wise man stroked his chin and thought. The farmer waited for him to speak.

"Do you have any cows?" asked the wise man.

"Yes, I have two cows," the farmer said.

"Then the answer is simple," the wise man said. "Tonight you must bring the cows into your house to stay with you, your wife, your seven children, and the horse."

"Are you sure?" the farmer asked. Surely the wise man did not mean what he was saying.

"Yes," said the wise man. "You must do as I tell you." So the farmer did as he was told.

The next morning the farmer returned to the wise man. He was even more upset.

"You are not so wise as you suppose!" the farmer said. "My house is louder than ever. The cows just moo morning, noon, and night, and the horse still kicks and neighs. I cannot stand it any longer." ◄✦►

◄✦►
Can you picture the cows in your mind?

97

The wise man stroked his chin and thought. The farmer waited for him to speak.

"Do you have any hens?" asked the wise man.

"Yes, I have some hens," said the farmer.

"Then the answer is simple," said the wise man. "Tonight you must bring the hens into your house to stay with you, your wife, your seven children, your horse, and your cows." The farmer could not believe his ears, but he did as he was told, for everyone knew the wise man to be very wise.

The next morning he returned to the wise
man. He was beside himself.

"You are not so wise as you suppose!" the
farmer said. "My house is louder than ever.
The hens just cluck and fight morning, noon,
and night! The cows still moo, and the horse
still neighs and kicks. My wife is upset, and the
children are crying. I cannot stand it any longer.
What can I do for some peace and quiet?" ◄►

"Well, take the animals out of your house,"
the wise man said. So the farmer did as he
was told, and once more he returned to the
wise man.

◄►
**Can you make a
picture in your
mind of what is
happening?**

"You *are* as wise as you suppose!" the farmer said. "You have turned my house into a home again! Now with all of the animals out, it is so nice and quiet! My family is happy, and I can hear myself think again. You have taught me to be happy with my house just the way it is. Thank you, thank you." ◆◆

And the wise man smiled.

◆◆
Can you make a picture in your mind of the house and how it looks now?

 Reader's **Response**

How would you have helped the farmer?

Not So Wise As You Suppose

 ## Questions

1. What problem did the farmer have?
2. Why was the farmer upset with the wise man's plan at first?
3. Why was the farmer happy at the end of the story?
4. What did the farmer mean when he said that his house was a home again? How did you get your answer?

 ## Writing to Learn

THINK AND VISUALIZE   Draw a picture of the farmer's house. Fill the house with the things you remember.

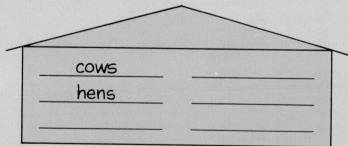

WRITE   Pretend *you* are in the farmer's house, too. Write about what it would be like to visit the farmer's house.

Houses

by Aileen Fisher

Houses are faces
(haven't you found?)
with their hats in the air,
and their necks in the ground.

Windows are noses,
windows are eyes,
and doors are the mouths
of a suitable size.

And a porch—or the place
where porches begin—
is just like a mustache
shading the chin.

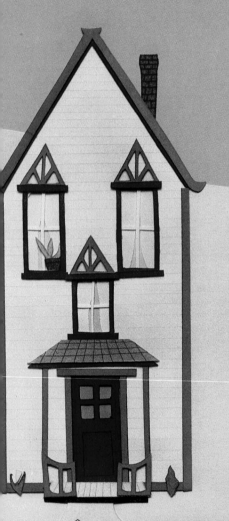

103

There are many ways to feel at home.
Luke shows you one way.

HOWDY!

by La Vada Weir

Luke was lonesome. He looked out of
his window and watched the people who
were waiting for the bus.

No one looked cheerful. No one
smiled. No one even spoke to anyone else.

READERS'
CHOICE
AWARD

Luke climbed up on a chair and got his new cowboy hat from the top shelf of the closet. He put on his hat and opened the apartment window.

"HOWDY!" Luke shouted to the people below. But just then the bus roared up to the bus stop. The people rushed to get on, and the bus roared away.

Luke went to his mother. She was on the telephone. "I want to go out with my cowboy hat," Luke said.

His mother smiled, patted him on the head with one hand, and kept on talking. Luke decided his mom wanted him to "run along." He went outside.

On the sidewalk, two boys were
playing with a red wagon.

"It's my turn!" yelled one of the boys.
He pulled at the wagon.

"No! It's my turn!" shouted the other
boy and tugged the wagon away.

Luke smiled his biggest smile.
Then he lifted his cowboy hat and
said, "HOWDY!"

The boys stopped tugging at the
wagon and stared at Luke. They were too
surprised to answer or smile back at him.

As they watched the boy in the big cowboy hat walk on down the street, the two boys began to smile at each other. They were still smiling when another boy came along.

"HOWDY!" the two boys said. And before long, they were all saying "howdy" to everyone and giving rides in their red wagon.

Next Luke went into an ice-cream store. A girl in a blue dress was trying to decide what kind of ice cream she wanted. The ice-cream man said, "Please, little girl, make up your mind."

Other people waited. Everyone was tired of waiting.

"HOWDY!" called Luke, lifting his hat and smiling. The people looked surprised, but no one said anything.

Luke turned and walked out the door. The people in the ice-cream store looked at each other's faces, and they began to smile.

"HOWDY!" said the man in a hat.

"HOWDY!" said a tall lady holding a large shopping bag. Soon everyone was smiling and talking to everyone else.

"I'll take vanilla," said the little girl in the blue dress. Then everyone decided they wanted vanilla, too.

The ice-cream man began to whistle a happy tune. The people in the shop were so cheerful that other people passing by the ice-cream store came in to see what was so special. When they were greeted with a smile and a "howdy," they became cheerful, too.

People came out of the ice-cream store. Everywhere they went, they smiled and called, "HOWDY!"

As he walked along, Luke passed a gas station. He shouted "HOWDY!" as he lifted his hat and walked on down the sidewalk.

Luke went into a supermarket and walked around. He smiled and said "HOWDY!" to everyone he saw.

After he left, everyone looked surprised. Suddenly everyone in the supermarket was smiling at everyone else.

Just as Luke was about to turn to go home, he heard someone shout, "Luke!"

His mother was behind him. She had run all the way around the block. "Luke!" she panted. "I have been looking everywhere for you."

"I wasn't lost. I was lonesome," Luke said.

"How can you be lonesome?" his mother asked. "I've never seen such friendly people. I followed a string of smiles and people saying 'howdy' all around the block."

Luke looked surprised. "No one said 'howdy' to me," he said.

Luke and his mother came to the steps of their apartment. "HOWDY!" called the people at the bus stop.

"HOWDY!" called a lady leaning out of her apartment window and watering her flowers.

"See what's happening?" said Luke's mother.

"It must be my hat," Luke decided.

"Must be," his mother nodded.

"It works like magic," Luke added. Then he lifted his cowboy hat, smiled, and said "HOWDY!" to everyone.

Everyone smiled back.

Luke's mother knew where the magic was, and she was very proud of Luke.

"HOWDY!"

 Reader's Response

If you wanted to make new friends in your neighborhood, how would you do it?

HOWDY!

 ## Questions

1. What did Luke tell his mother he wanted to do?
2. How did Luke feel? How do you know?
3. How did people feel after they met Luke?
4. Why did Luke think his cowboy hat was magic? Was Luke right?

 ## Writing to Learn

THINK AND IMAGINE   Pretend you are walking along the street and you meet Luke. Luke says, "Howdy!" What will you say?

Howdy!

WRITE   Draw a speech balloon on your paper. Inside it, write the words you would say to Luke.

Pueblos
of the Southwest

This article is about pueblos. A pueblo is a special kind of home.

Some Native Americans who live in the Southwest got their name from the kind of homes and villages they built. Their villages were made of houses that were joined together to make big buildings.

Long ago, Spanish people came upon the villages of these Native Americans. The Spanish people used the word *pueblo* (pwe'-blō) to name these villages. The word *pueblo* is a Spanish word meaning "village." The Native Americans who lived in these villages became known as the Pueblo people.

by Anna Westcott

Pueblo buildings had many homes that were joined together. The first ones were built nearly seven hundred years ago. Most Pueblo buildings were two or three stories high. They were made from things that the people could find in the dry lands of the Southwest, such as earth, stone, and some wood. The Pueblo people used ladders to get into their own houses and to get to the other homes in the large Pueblo village.

How Pueblo Homes Were Made

When a new home was added on to the pueblo, the family built its house using the old ways. The Pueblo men built the walls of the house with stone and mud. They had to cut the stone and put it in place. By putting stones one on top of the other, they built the walls. The mud held the stones together. Then the men put wood on top of the walls to start the flat roof.

The Pueblo women finished the house. They covered the wood on the roof with poles, leaving an opening. The family would use this opening to get into the house. Next, the women covered the poles with branches and grasses. Then they covered the roof with mud. When the mud was dry, the women covered the roof with earth. Then they covered the stone walls with clay.

117

The Pueblo family joined their new home to the home of the woman's mother and father. When the other girls in the family grew up, they also built new homes and joined them together. In this way, the homes made one big building.

When the Pueblo people joined their homes together, they left a space in the middle for everyone to share. They called this space the plaza. When they looked down from their roof, the family could see everything in the plaza. From the roof, they could watch the dances the people did at special times.

Inside a Pueblo Home

A Pueblo family went into their home by climbing down through the opening on the roof, using a ladder. Once inside, there would be just one room for the family to share. This one room was used mainly for sleeping, because most of a Pueblo family's time was spent outside. There were no tables, chairs, or beds. The family used blankets, rugs, and sheepskins for sitting and sleeping. A fireplace kept the room warm.

The most important thing found in a Pueblo home was the woman's grinding stone. The woman used the grinding stone to crush corn and other foods for cooking.

Feathers were also important to the Pueblo people. The men put four feathers on the ground before building the walls of a house. People also hung feathers in their homes. They believed that the feathers would help to keep them safe.

Pueblos Today

Pueblo villages today are different from those of long ago. Today you can see Pueblo homes that are one or two stories high. They also have many rooms. These newer homes have doors and windows, too. They are a lot like the homes you live in.

Some Pueblo people have moved away from their villages. They have built homes in the city near their work. Although they have moved away, the Pueblo people still feel that village life is important. They return to their pueblo to take part in village life and in the special Pueblo dances held in the plaza.

Reader's Response

What would be the best thing about living in a pueblo home? Tell why you think this.

Pueblos
of the Southwest

 ## Questions

1. What does the word *pueblo* mean?
2. Why didn't the Pueblo people use wood to build their homes? How do you know?
3. How are today's pueblo villages different from those in the past?
4. Some Pueblo people have moved away from the pueblos. Why do you think they still visit the villages?

 ## Writing to Learn

THINK AND CREATE   What kind of home would you like to create? Copy this chart on your paper.

What I do there	What it would be like
Eat	
Play	
Sleep	
Read	

WRITE   Write a sentence about each part of the home you create.

In this story, a boy tells how he feels about his pueblo home.

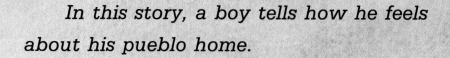

My
PUEBLO
Home

by Ann Nolan Clark
from In My Mother's House

This is my Mother's house;
My Father made it.
He made it with adobe bricks;
He made it strong;

He made it big;
He made it high;
My Mother's house,
I live in it.

AWARD
WINNING
AUTHOR

This is my Mother's house;
My Mother plastered it
With brown clay;
On the outside
My Mother plastered it.

The inside walls are white;
My Mother made them white;
The floor is smooth;
My Mother made it smooth,
For me to live there.

In my Mother's house
There is a fireplace:
The fireplace holds the fire.
On dark nights the fire is bright;
On cold nights the fire is warm.
The fire is always there,
To help me see,
To keep me warm.

In my Mother's house
There are the grinding stones:
The big, flat holding stone,
The small rubbing stone;
The grinding stones,
My Mother's grinding stones.

On the floor
Beside her stones
My Mother kneels,
And with her hands
She grinds the corn;
Yellow corn and blue corn
My Mother grinds
For me to eat.

My Mother's house,
It does not stand alone.
Its sister houses are around it;
Its sister houses are close to it.

Like holding hands,
The houses stand close together
Around the plaza.

Houses are the stay-in places,
But the plaza
Is the live-in place
For all the people.

In my Mother's house
All day
I play and work;
All night
I sleep.

The walls come close around me
In a good way.
I can see them;
I can feel them;
I live with them.

This house is good to me,
It keeps me;
I like it,
My Mother's house.

◆ LIBRARY LINK ◆

Did you know that some houses can move from one place to another? Read The Little House by Virginia Lee Burton.

Reader's Response

Would you like to live in a pueblo?
Why or why not?

My PUEBLO Home

Questions

1. What did the boy's mother do to help build the house?
2. What helped the boy to see and to stay warm in his house?
3. What did the boy mean when he said, "Houses are the stay-in places, but the plaza is the live-in place"?
4. How did the boy compare his house to a family? How did you figure out your answer?

Writing to Learn

THINK AND DESCRIBE Close your eyes and make a picture of a pueblo house in your mind. Draw a frame. Write words to name things in the house.

Word Picture

blankets
smooth walls

WRITE Write to describe what you would see in a pueblo house.

Understanding Social Studies Words

In social studies books, you learn about places where people live. You also learn about places where people work and play. Sometimes important words are used to describe these places.

Your social studies book helps you learn these important words in two ways. First, your book may have lists of important words. Second, your book may show important words in **dark letters.**

The meaning of the word in dark letters is usually given in the sentences that follow the word.

How to Learn Social Studies Words

Use the word list.

The word list below is from a social studies book. The list has words you need to know as you read. Pictures may help you learn about the words. What are the words in the list?

community   neighborhood

The picture of the *community* shows a fire station, a gas station, and places where people live. The picture shows that a community is a place where people live and work.

The other picture shows that a *neighborhood* is a place where people live.

Watch for words in dark letters.

As you read a chapter, look for words in dark type. The sentences that come after usually tell what these words mean. Pictures also help to make the meaning of the word clear.

Find the social studies word in dark type below. What does it mean?

In some communities there are many **neighborhoods**. A neighborhood is a part of a community. The people in a neighborhood are neighbors. Neighbors sometimes help each other.

As You Read   Read the following pages from a social studies book. Answer the questions on page 139.

Learning About Communities

community

neighborhood

city

apartment building

factory

museum

suburb

town

What is a city?

A **city** is a large community where
many people live and work.
Often, people in cities live in **apartment buildings**.
An apartment building is a home for many families.

People work at many kinds of jobs in a city.
They work in office buildings, stores, and
factories.
A factory is a place where things are made.
This factory worker is making toy cars.

All cities have places where people have fun.
These people are enjoying a baseball game.

There are parks in most cities.
People in this park are
putting on a circus show.
There is plenty of space for
other people to sit and watch.

There is a zoo in most large cities.
Animals are fun to watch.
Some animals are fun to ride.

Most cities have at least
one **museum**.
A museum is a building
where different groups
of things are shown.
Every museum has many
interesting things to see.
Museums help us learn
how people lived long ago.
They give us ideas about
what the future may be like.

What is a suburb?

Most large cities have communities all around them.
A community just outside a city is called a **suburb**.
Suburbs are usually smaller than cities.
They are often less crowded.
In suburbs most homes are for one family.

Using What You Have Learned

1. Look at page 133. What can you learn about a museum from the picture?

2. Look at page 137. What else did you learn about museums?

3. What are the important words on page 134? How can you tell they are important?

4. What is the meaning of the word *factory?* You may want to look at pages 133 and 135 for ideas.

5. What is the meaning of the word *suburb?* What are two ways the social studies book helps you learn about the word *suburb?*

Examples and excerpts are from *Communities and Their Needs, Silver Burdett & Ginn Social Studies,* © 1988.

READING FICTION

Literature:

Following a Story

In most stories, several things happen. In "Keep the Lights Burning, Abbie," Abbie's Papa left to get medicine for Mama. While he was gone, Abbie kept the lamps in the lighthouse burning. She did this so that ships at sea would be safe.

How to Follow a Story

Were you able to follow what happened in "Keep the Lights Burning, Abbie"? A good way to follow a story is to make a story map. A story map helps you see the important things that happen. To make a story map, you should ask yourself these questions:

1. Who is the story about?
2. When or where does the story take place?
3. What is the problem?
4. How does the story end?

Here is a story map for "Keep the Lights Burning, Abbie."

Who:	Abbie, Papa, Mama, Esther, Lydia
Where:	A lighthouse
Problem:	Abbie must keep the lighthouse lamps burning so that ships will be safe.
Ending:	Papa returns.

Read and Enjoy

The next story is called "The House That Nobody Wanted." As you read, think about what information you would put into a map of the story.

The little old house in this story is so
gray. Maybe no one will want it.

The House That Nobody Wanted

written by Lilian Moore
illustrated by Arnold Lobel

There was once a little house that stood
on a hill. It was an old house—very old and
very gray. It had gray doors and gray
windows, gray walls and a gray fence.

A little old man and a little old woman
lived in this house. And they had lived there
for a long time.

142

The old man and the old woman did not
go out much. But one fine day they made
up their minds to visit their friends.

So they got into their little old car and
rode away. They rode uphill and downhill
and then uphill and downhill again.

143

And at last they saw the house of their
friends. It was a little red house with white
doors and windows, and all around it flowers
and green things were growing.

The little old man and the little old
woman had a good time with their friends.
Then they got into their little old car and
went home. They rode uphill and downhill,
then uphill and downhill again. And at last
they came to their own house.

"My!" said the old woman. "Our house
is *very* gray, isn't it?"

"And there is nothing green to see when we look out," said the old man.

"Let's sell this house!" said the old woman. "Then we can buy a pretty house!"

". . . with grass and flowers growing around it!" said the old man.

So the little old man and the little old woman tried to sell their house.

First a man came to look.

"No," he said. "This house is too gray for me. I like a red house." And he went away.

"Oh dear!" said the little old woman.

"Let's paint the house red," said the old man. "Then maybe the next one will buy it."

So the little old man and the little old woman painted the house red. Soon after, a woman came to look.

"I like a house that has white windows and white doors," she said. "I like a white fence and a white gate, too." And she went away.

So the little old man and the little old woman painted the windows white. Then they painted the doors and the gate and the fence white, too.

Soon after that, a man and a woman came to see the house. They liked the outside.

"But it is so gray inside," said the woman. And they went away.

So this time the little old man and the little old woman painted the walls inside the house. They painted some walls yellow and some walls blue.

Soon another man came to see the house.

"This is a pretty house," he said. "But I am looking for a home with a garden." And he, too, went away.

The old man and the old woman began to work on a garden. Soon green grass was growing.

Then one day there were flowers—red and purple and yellow—growing all around the house.

"Now," said the old woman. "Someone will want to buy this house! Then at last we can buy the house *we* want."

The old man looked around.

He said, "What kind of house *do* we want?"

"Well," she said. "We want a pretty house."

"Painted inside and out?" he asked.

"Oh yes!" said the old woman.

"With grass and flowers growing around it?" asked the old man.

"Oh yes!" said the little old woman.

The old man laughed.

"Look around," he told her.

So the little old woman looked around. She saw a red house with white windows and doors, a white fence and a white gate, too. Inside the house she saw bright yellow and blue walls. Outside she saw grass and flowers growing.

"Well!" she said, surprised. "This is a pretty house, isn't it?"

"This is just the house we want!" said the old man.

So the little old man and the little old woman went right on living in the little old house on the hill.

Only it wasn't a little gray house anymore.

◆ LIBRARY LINK ◆

This story is from the book Junk Day on Juniper Street *by Lilian Moore. Look for* "The Peanut Butter Sandwich" *in this book, too.*

 Reader's **Response**

Would you like to live in the little gray house? Tell why or why not.

Writing About a Favorite Place

The stories you have read tell about different kinds of houses. There were pueblo houses, farm houses, apartment houses, and even a house that nobody wanted. All of these places were special to the people who lived in them.

Sometimes a house can make you feel happy because of the people or things that are there. Other places can make you feel happy, too.

Now you can write about your own special place.

Prewriting

Think about your favorite places. Is one of them your kitchen or your back yard? Maybe your favorite place is under a tree. Why do you like to be there?

Choose one place you will describe in a paragraph. Draw a picture of it.

Writing

Look at your picture. What words describe your special place? Can you think of words that tell what you see, smell, or feel?

Copy the chart below and write a word in each box that tells what you see, hear, smell, or feel in your special place.

Use your picture and your chart to write sentences about your special place.

A Place Where I Like to Be	
What I see	
What I hear	
What I smell	
What I feel	

Revising

Read what you wrote. Did you use the words from your chart? Cross out any words you don't need.

Proofreading

Check your paper again. If you aren't sure how to spell a word, look it up in a dictionary.

Make a neat copy. Add a title.

Publishing

Paste your picture and your sentences on a large sheet of colored paper. Hang your picture.

Fixing up a House

Remember how a man and his wife changed their house in "The House That Nobody Wanted?" Your group will make a list of ideas to fix up this house.

To help you work well together, do one or more of these jobs:

♦ See that everyone gets a chance to talk.

♦ Ask people questions.

♦ Write a list of ideas.

Together talk about what you might do to fix up the house. Everyone should give ideas. Agree on what color the house will be. Would you make a garden for the house? Would a pet live there? What else does the house need? Make a list of ideas. Everyone should agree on the list.

BOOKS TO ENJOY

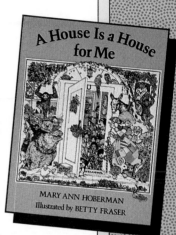

A House Is a House for Me by Mary Ann Hoberman *(Viking, 1977)* Read about places where animals and people live.

Evan's Corner by Elizabeth Starr Hill *(Holt, Rinehart & Winston, 1967)* Evan lives in a small apartment with his parents and three sisters and two brothers. More than anything else, he longs for a place he can call his own.

The Little House by Virginia Lee Burton *(Houghton Mifflin, 1942)* This story follows the life of a house as its surroundings change.

Always Room for One More by Sorche Nic Leodhas *(Holt, Rinehart & Winston, 1965)* This funny story shows you what can happen when you keep inviting people to come to your house!

GIFTS AND TREASURES

*G*ifts and treasures can come in many shapes and forms.

What is a gift? What is a treasure?

THE HUNDRED FLOWERS,
ink and colors on silk, after Yün Shou-p'ing, Chinese, 18th century

155

Daniel wants to make something special.

Daniel's Duck

by Clyde Robert Bulla

Jeff and Daniel were brothers. They lived in a cabin on a mountain in Tennessee.

Jeff had a good knife. He could carve with it. He could carve things out of wood. He made a dish. Then he made a cup. His mother and father were proud. "Some day," they said, "you may be as good as Henry Pettigrew."

Henry Pettigrew lived in the valley. They had never seen him, but they had seen his work. He was a woodcarver. Some said he was the best woodcarver in Tennessee.

AMERICAN
LIBRARY
ASSOCIATION
1978

Henry Pettigrew carved animals. His birds looked as if they could fly. His horses looked as if they could run. All his animals looked real. Jeff and his brother had seen some of them in town.

"I want to carve an animal like Henry Pettigrew's," said Jeff. "But animals are hard to do."

"I want to carve an animal, too," said Daniel.

"You're not old enough," said Jeff.

"Yes, I am," said Daniel. "I could carve one if I had a good knife and some wood."

"It takes more than a good knife and some wood," said Jeff. "You have to know how. It's hard to carve an animal."

"I know how," said Daniel.

"Let's see if you do," said his father. He gave Daniel a knife like Jeff's. He gave him a block of wood.

It was winter. The nights were long. "This is a good time to sit by the fire and carve," said Jeff. "I'm going to make something for the spring fair."

Every spring there was a fair in the valley. It was time for people to meet after the long winter. It was a time to show things that they had made. Sometimes they would sell what they had made. Sometimes they would trade with one another.

On winter nights father made moccasins to take to the fair. Mother cut bits of cloth. She sewed them together to make a quilt.

"I'm going to make a box for the fair," said Jeff. "I'm going to carve little moons on the lid." He said to his brother, "What are you going to make?"

"I have to think," said Daniel.

Days went by. Then Daniel began to carve. "What are you making?" asked Jeff.

"You'll see," said Daniel.

One night Jeff looked at what Daniel was carving. He saw a neck and a head. He saw a wing. "Now I see," he said. "It's a bird."

"It's a duck," said Daniel.

"You're not doing it right," said Jeff. "Its head is on backward."

"I want it that way," said Daniel. "My duck is looking back."

"That's no way to do it," said Jeff.

Father said, "Let him do it his way."

Spring came. It was time for the fair. Mother had made her quilt for the fair. Father had made three pairs of moccasins. Jeff's box was done.

"It took a long time," Jeff said.

"My duck took a long time, too," said Daniel.

"Are you sure you want to take it to the fair?" asked Jeff.

"Yes," said Daniel.

They drove into town. There were people everywhere. Everyone had come to the fair.

Father took the quilt and the moccasins. He took Jeff's box and Daniel's duck. He left them at the hall.

They walked down the street. They saw the river. They talked with friends.

Father said, "The hall is open."

They went to the show. There were pictures that people had made. There were quilts and rugs and baskets. There were dolls and caps.

"Where are the wood carvings?" asked Daniel.

"Over here," said Jeff.

They went to the end of the hall. On a small table was a carved deer. It was so beautiful that people were quiet when they looked at it. Everyone knew it had been done by Henry Pettigrew.

On a big table were the carvings that others had done. Many people were looking at the carvings. They were laughing.

"What are they laughing at?" asked Daniel. Jeff didn't answer.

Someone said, "Look at the duck!"

Someone else said, "That duck is so funny!"

More people came to look. More people were laughing. Now Daniel knew. They were laughing at his duck. He wanted to go away. He wanted to hide. Then he was angry. He went to the table. He picked up his duck and ran with it.

He ran out of the hall. Someone was running after him. He ran faster. He came to the river. He started to throw the duck as far as he could. But he could not throw it.

A man had hold of his arm. The man asked, "What are you doing with that duck?"

"I'm going to throw it in the river!" said Daniel.

"You can't do that," said the man.

"I can if I want to," said Daniel. "It's mine."

"Did you make it?" asked the man.

"Yes," said Daniel.

"Why were you going to throw it away?" asked the man.

"They all laughed at it," said Daniel.

"Listen to me," said the man. "There are different ways of laughing. The people *liked* your duck. They laughed because they liked it."

"No. It's ugly," said Daniel.

"It *isn't* ugly. It's a good duck. It made me feel happy. That's why I laughed."

The man was not laughing now. "You're hot and tired," he said. "Come and rest in the shade."

They sat under a tree. "Would you sell your duck?" asked the man.

"Who would buy it?" asked Daniel.

"I might think of someone," said the man.

A boy and girl came up to them. "How are you, Mr. Pettigrew?" they asked.

"I'm fine," said the man. The boy and girl went on.

Daniel said, "You're Henry Pettigrew!"

"Yes," said the man. "I'm a woodcarver, too."

"I know that," said Daniel.

He was holding his duck. He looked down at it. It wasn't ugly. It was a good duck. Henry Pettigrew had said so, and he knew.

"I saw your deer," said Daniel.

"I made it last winter," said the man. "I've made lots of things. My house is full of them."

Daniel said, "I wish—" and then he stopped.

"What do you wish?" asked the man.

"I wish I could see the things you've made," said Daniel.

"I'll show them to you," said the man. "Maybe today, after the fair. Do you want to go back to the fair now?"

"Yes," said Daniel. They got up. The man was looking at the duck.

"Will you sell it to me?" he asked.

"No," said Daniel. He held the duck a little longer. Then he gave it to Henry Pettigrew.

◆ LIBRARY LINK ◆

Other books by Clyde Robert Bulla that you may enjoy are Indian Hill, Down the Mississippi, *and* Riding the Pony Express.

 Reader's Response

Do you think Daniel's duck was special? Tell why you think this.

Daniel's Duck

 ## Questions

1. Why did Jeff's parents compare his work to Henry Pettigrew's work?
2. How did Daniel feel when people laughed at his duck? What did he do?
3. Henry Pettigrew said there are different ways of laughing. What did he mean?
4. Why did Daniel give his duck to Henry Pettigrew?
5. Do you think Daniel will carve something else out of wood? Why do you think so?

 ## Writing to Learn

THINK AND DECIDE Daniel carved a duck. If you could carve, what would you make? Here is a picture of a block of wood. Draw a picture of what you would like to carve.

WRITE Write sentences that tell about your carving.

*Giving a gift is fun—even when you
can give only a part of it.*

The Train Set

written and illustrated
by Pat Hutchins

There was a train set in the window
of Mindy's Store. Every morning on his
way to school, Peter stopped to look at it.

"That sure is the finest train set I've ever seen," he would say. "Just look at that engine, that coach, that flat car, that caboose, and that track. A fine train set like that must cost a lot of money."

"Come on," said his brothers and sisters. "We'll be late for school."

"What are you getting Peter for his birthday?" the children asked Ma and Pa. "He sure wants that train set in Mindy's window!"

"We're not telling," said Ma. "No one can keep a secret in this family."

"We've got ten dollars to spend," said Pa. "Let's go and see what the train costs."

"How much is that train set in the window?" Ma asked.

"Thirty dollars," said Mr. Mindy.

"Too bad," Ma sighed. "We were hoping it would be closer to ten."

"The engine costs ten dollars," said Mr. Mindy. "It's a grand engine!"

"It sure is," Pa agreed, "but not much use on its own."

Ma picked up the engine. "Well," she said, "it would be a start."

"What are you getting Peter for his birthday?" Anna asked Tony. "He sure wants that train set."

"I'm not telling," said Tony. "No one can keep a secret in this family."

I've saved eight dollars from helping at the drugstore, thought Tony. I'll go and see what the train set costs.

"How much is the train set in the window?" Tony asked.

"Thirty dollars for the set," said Mr. Mindy, "but we just sold the engine."

"Oh!" said Tony. "I was hoping it might be around eight."

"The track costs eight dollars," said Mr. Mindy. "It's the best sort of track."

"It certainly is the best sort of track,"
Tony agreed, "but not much use on
its own."

"It's a start," said Mr. Mindy.

"What are you giving Peter for his
birthday?" Frank asked Anna. "He's crazy
for that train set."

"I'm not telling," said Anna. "No one
can keep a secret in this family."

I've saved five dollars from running
errands, thought Anna. I'll go and see
what it costs.

"How much is that train set in the
window?" Anna asked.

"Thirty dollars for the set," said Mr. Mindy, "but I've just sold the engine and the track."

"I've only got five dollars," said Anna.

"The coach is five," said Mr. Mindy. "It's a beautiful coach."

"It's a beautiful coach all right," Anna agreed. "And I guess it's a start!"

"What are you giving Peter for his birthday?" Maria asked Frank. "He's mad for that train in Mindy's."

"I'm not telling," said Frank. "No one can keep a secret in this family."

I've got four dollars saved, thought Frank. I'll go and see what it costs.

"What happened to that train in the window?" Frank asked. "I've got four dollars, and I wanted to buy it."

"I've just sold the engine, the track, and the coach," said Mr. Mindy, "but the caboose is four dollars."

"It's a very fine caboose," said Frank, "but not much use on its own."

"It's a start," said Mr. Mindy.

Maria had three dollars saved. I'll go and see what that train set costs, she thought.

"How much is that train set you had in the window?" she asked.

"Thirty dollars for the set," said Mr. Mindy, "but I've just sold the engine, the track, the coach, and the caboose. The flat car is all that is left. But that is three dollars."

"Well," said Maria, "a flat car's not much use on its own, but I'll take it."

The next day Peter woke up very early. Everyone else was still asleep. I'll just go and look at the train set, he thought, before everyone gets up. But when he got there the train had gone. "Too bad," Peter sighed, and he walked slowly home.

"What's wrong?" asked Ma as he opened the door. "It's your birthday, and you look as if you've found a nickel and lost a quarter."

"I've just been to Mindy's," said Peter, "and the train set's gone."

"Is it?" said Ma and Pa. "Well, here's the engine. Happy birthday!"

"Gosh!" said Tony. "I've bought you the track!"

"And I bought you the coach!" cried Anna.

"I bought you the caboose!" shouted Frank.

"How about that!" screamed Maria. "I bought you the flat car!"

"I told you!" said Ma, as Peter stared at the parcels. "No one can keep a secret in this family. He hasn't even opened them yet!" But he soon did, and it certainly was the finest train set he'd ever seen.

◆ LIBRARY LINK ◆

This story is from the book The Best Train Set Ever *by Pat Hutchins. You might enjoy reading the other stories in this book, too.*

Reader's Response

Do you think each family member should have kept the birthday secret? Tell why or why not.

The Train Set

 Questions

1. Where did Peter go every morning on his way to school?
2. Why wasn't the train in the window when Frank went to Mr. Mindy's store?
3. What could you tell about Peter's family from the story? What details told you this?
4. When Peter saw the train set, what do you think he did?

 Writing to Learn

THINK AND DECIDE Think about words that tell how Peter felt on the morning of his birthday. Draw a square on your paper. Draw puzzle pieces in the square. In each piece, write a word that tells how Peter felt when he saw each present.

WRITE Write about a day when something good happened to you. Tell how you felt.

Lee Bennett Hopkins
INTERVIEWS

Aliki

When Aliki was five, her teacher told her parents that she would be an artist someday. Aliki had made two pictures—one of her own family and one of Peter Rabbit's family. Her drawings were so good that everyone told Aliki how much they liked them. She felt really special.

"So much fuss was made over the drawings," said Aliki, "that I, too, knew that I would grow up to become an artist."

Aliki grew up in Philadelphia, a city in Pennsylvania. Her parents sent her to study art on Saturdays, and she also studied piano.

Aliki kept on drawing all the years she was in school. "I drew all the time," she said, "even during math class."

Later, after high school, Aliki studied art in Philadelphia. After she finished art school, she worked as an artist in many jobs. Aliki worked on ads, and she even drew her own greeting cards.

When she was twenty-seven years old, Aliki visited Italy. There she met a man named Franz Brandenberg. A year later she married him, and they moved to Switzerland.

In Switzerland, Aliki wrote her first book, *The Story of William Tell*. Then Aliki and Franz moved to New York. Aliki went on to write and draw pictures for many children's books. This was what she liked to do best.

Aliki and Franz are the parents of two children, Jason and Alexa. When her children were little, they helped Aliki see things the way children do. In a way, they helped her to write better books for children.

Often Aliki had to spend a lot of time working on a book. Sometimes she could not always get dinner on the table in time. "But now," she says, "Jason and Alexa are both good cooks!"

Today Aliki and Franz live in London, England, where she still writes and draws. She says, "My work is my life."

Music is important to Aliki, too. Her hands cannot draw without music.

The next story you will read is called "The Story of Johnny Appleseed." Aliki wrote it. She also drew the pictures.

Reader's Response

Would you like to do what Aliki does? Why or why not?

LEE BENNETT HOPKINS INTERVIEWS

Aliki

Questions

1. How did Aliki become a good artist?
2. Which did Aliki do first—learn to draw or learn to write children's stories?
3. Aliki said her children helped her see things the way children do. How did you know what she meant?
4. What special skills does a writer need?
5. How did Aliki's parents help her become an artist?

Writing to Learn

THINK AND PREDICT   When Aliki was a little girl, she discovered she liked to draw. What do you like to do? Draw a picture of yourself doing what you like to do now.

Here I am doing what
I like to do.

WRITE   Think about your picture. Write about something you want to do when you grow up.

181

Vocabulary:
Homophones

Some words sound the same—like *sea* and *see*. But they have different meanings and different spellings. The word *sea* means "a body of salt water." The word *see* means "to use the eyes, or to look at."

Words that sound the same but have different meanings and spellings are called *homophones*. It is important to recognize homophones so that you spell them correctly when you write.

Read these sentences with homophones, from the story "Daniel's Duck." Which words sound the same?

He could carve things out of *wood*.
"*Would* you sell your duck?" asked the man.

Wood and *would* sound the same, but they have different meanings and different spellings. Which homophone means "the hard part of a tree"?

When you read words that sound the same in a story, look at the other words in the sentence. Read the sentence again. The other words can help you figure out the meaning of the homophone.

Read aloud the sentences below.

No *one* in this family can keep a secret.
The Jets *won* the baseball game.

The words *one* and *won* are homophones. They sound the same. But, as you know, they have different meanings and different spellings.

Using What You Have Learned

Find the homophone in each sentence. Then write your own sentence for each homophone.

1. Rita likes to write to her grandparents.
2. She wants to spell all her words in the right way.

Long ago, John Chapman gave a special gift to his country.

READERS'
CHOICE
AWARD

The Story Of

Johnny Appleseed

One day, after a long walk, John Chapman sat under a tree to rest. He felt the warm sun on his back and the fresh grass under his feet. John took an apple from his sack and ate it. And when he had finished, he looked in his hand at what was left—just five brown seeds. And John thought: If one collected seeds and planted them, our land would soon be filled with apple trees.

In their covered wagons, the pioneers made the long, hard journey through the wilderness. They wanted to build new lives for themselves in a new part of the country. John Chapman went, too. But he did not go in a covered wagon, like the other pioneers. He walked in his bare feet. He carried only a large sack on his back, filled with apple seeds, and his cooking pan on his head.

*written and illustrated
by Aliki*

185

As he walked, John planted seeds. He gave a small sack of seeds to everyone he saw on his journey. Soon everyone who knew him called him Johnny Appleseed.

Sometimes Johnny stopped for many weeks, helping the pioneers. They cleared the land. They built homes. They planted many apple trees. When they were finished, Johnny walked on to help others. But he always came back to see his friends.

Everyone loved Johnny Appleseed, most of all the children. When Johnny rested from his planting, the children sat around him, listening to all the stories he had collected on his journey.

Johnny Appleseed walked alone. He slept out of doors, in the woods or by the river. He met foxes, birds and deer, and sometimes, even a wolf. They were all his friends.

One day, as Johnny was eating lunch, three little bear cubs ran from behind a tree. When the mother bear came and saw them playing together, she sat and watched. She knew Johnny Appleseed would not harm her cubs.

Johnny made friends with many Indians on the way. He gave them seeds and special plants, which they used as medicine.

On and on Johnny walked, planting as he went. When he needed more seeds, he collected sacks of seeds from the cider mills. Everyone saved apple seeds for Johnny.

Many years passed. Johnny Appleseed walked on. He visited his friends and was pleased to see the many apple trees which covered the land. And he was happy.

But then, one year, there was a long, cold winter. When spring should have come, snow was still on the ground, and frost was on the trees. Johnny could not sleep or eat. He was afraid his trees would die.

As he was walking through the trees one day, Johnny Appleseed fell to the ground. He was very ill. After some time, an Indian mother and her child passed and saw Johnny on the ground. Quickly the boy ran for help. Johnny was carried to their village, not far away.

For many days he lay ill. The Indians gave him medicine and took care of him.

And one day, Johnny Appleseed opened his eyes. He smiled at his Indian friends. He knew they had saved his life. He saw that the sun was warm, and the frost had left the trees. Spring had come at last, and Johnny was well again. But he never forgot his Indian friends and went to see them many times.

Johnny Appleseed, the gentle pioneer, lived for many years, planting apple trees wherever he went. We can still see them today. They are large and old and heavy with apples. They are the gift Johnny Appleseed gave to his country and to you and to me.

◆ LIBRARY LINK ◆

Other stories by Aliki that you will find in the library are At Mary Bloom's *and* We Are Best Friends.

Reader's Response

Would you like to do what Johnny Appleseed did?

The Story Of
Johnny Appleseed

Questions

1. What was Johnny Appleseed's real name?
2. Why did Johnny Appleseed want to plant apple trees all over the country?
3. How was Johnny Appleseed like other pioneers? How was he different?
4. What kind of person was Johnny Appleseed? Explain how you got your answer.

Writing to Learn

THINK AND IMAGINE Johnny Appleseed filled our land with apple trees. Draw a gift you would like to give our country.

WRITE Write a sentence that tells why your gift is an important one.

America's First Great Readers

▲ William H. McGuffey

One hundred and fifty years ago, when your great-great-great-great grandparents went to school, they probably used the *McGuffey Readers*. From Maine to California, almost all American children learned to read from this set of books. These famous readers were published in the 1800s by William H. McGuffey.

Only some children went to school when they were six years old. In those days, some people didn't begin school until they were older. That didn't matter. They all started with Book 1, which had "Mary Had a Little Lamb." There were six readers in all.

▲
McGuffey Readers were used by children 150 years ago.

▲This illustration is taken from McGuffey's *First Eclectic Reader.*

▲ "The Lame Dog" is Lesson 21.

Some of the stories taught lessons about being a good child. Other lessons were about words and sounds.

Some things about schools are still the same as they were when your great-great-great-great grandparents used *McGuffey Readers.* There are teachers and children, classes and lessons. But now there are many, many more books, with colorful pictures to look at and interesting stories to read.

193

Study Skill:

ABC Order

Johnny Appleseed planted apple trees everywhere he went. Pretend you are going to buy some seeds to plant in your own garden.

Look at the first sign in this plant store. The names of these seeds begin with *different* letters in alphabetical order.

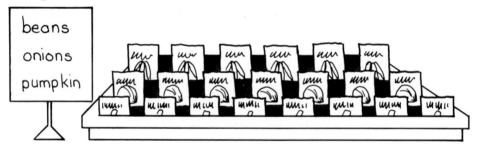

beans
onions
pumpkin

Now look at the second sign. The names of these seeds begin with the *same* letter. But they are also in alphabetical order. How can you tell?

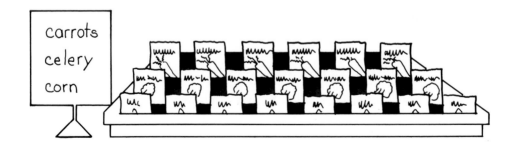

carrots
celery
corn

194

Steps to Put Words into ABC Order

Look at the first letter of each word.

1. If the first letters in the words are different, put the words in alphabetical order—by the *first* letter.

2. If the first letters in the words are the same, look at the second letter. Then you can put the words in alphabetical order—by the *second* letter.

Using What You Have Learned

Look at these names. On your paper, write the names in alphabetical order.

Aliki   Abbie   Anna

As You Read

The next article you will read is called "The Smithsonian Institution." As you read, look for the words *artist, museum,* and *famous.*

After you have finished reading, find these words in the glossary in the back of your book, using alphabetical order to find them.

The Smithsonian

Institution

by Walter Dean Myers

The Smithsonian Institution in Washington, D.C., is America's biggest treasure chest.

Imagine walking inside a great big treasure chest. Museums are just like treasure chests. They are places where you can see and learn many interesting things about our world. You can see artists' works, such as paintings and sculptures, in art museums. You can see how people lived in the past in history museums. You can see science exhibits in science museums. But can you imagine a place where you can see *all* of these wonderful things? You can find them all at the Smithsonian Institution in Washington, D.C.

The Smithsonian Institution is one of our country's greatest museums. It is made up of fourteen different museums. You will find treasures from all over the world at the Smithsonian. Now let's take a journey through some of the wonderful museums there. First we will stop at the National Museum of American Art.

Here we are at the National Museum of American Art. You can see many exhibits of paintings, sculptures, and other works of art by American artists.

In one gallery you can see George Catlin's famous paintings of Native Americans. George Catlin was a pioneer artist who went to the West in the 1830s. While he was there, he painted many pictures of Native Americans and their everyday life. These paintings help people today to imagine what the life of Native Americans was like.

These paintings are in the Catlin gallery.

Your great, great grandparents may have attended a school like this one.

The National Museum of American History has exhibits about the history of America. There are all kinds of things that have to do with American life. You can see what American homes and schools were like long ago. You can even see the first Star-Spangled Banner.

There are many famous American inventions in this museum. The first record player and some of the very first light bulbs are here.

You can also see some of the first cars that were built. Cars were different eighty years ago. At that time, people rode very high up off the ground. Cars were not nearly as fast as they are today. Some of the most famous race cars are here, too. You can see cars that went fast enough to win the world's biggest races!

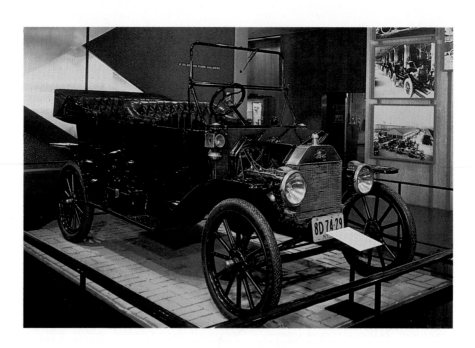

This Model T Ford was built in 1913.

The National Museum of Natural History

A boy holds the Hickory Horn Devil caterpillar.

The Museum of Natural History has exhibits about the plants, animals and minerals of America. You can see the different kinds of animals that live in the deserts, forests, mountains and prairies of our country.

The Insect Zoo is part of this museum. You can see live insects, and you can even touch and hold some of them.

A tour guide answers questions about an air and space exhibit.

Since the beginning of time, people have wished that they could fly. In this science museum you will find many inventions that have to do with flight. Kites of every color hang from the roof. There are huge, beautiful hot-air balloons that people have floated in through the air.

202

You will also find famous airplanes here. Have you heard of Charles Lindbergh? He was the first man to cross the Atlantic Ocean alone in an airplane. You can see that airplane here.

But this museum isn't only about airplanes. It's also about space. You can see space suits, and you can even touch a moon rock.

These exhibits honor the United States Space program.

Other Things to See

The National Museum of American Art, the National Museum of American History, and the National Air and Space Museum are just some of the museums at the Smithsonian Institution. There is much more to see, like a zoo and a sculpture garden. The Smithsonian is filled with many interesting treasures. You could spend weeks in this wonderful place and still not see everything!

You can even see Dorothy's famous red shoes from the movie The Wizard of Oz.

Reader's Response

Which part of the Smithsonian Institution would you like to visit? Tell why.

The Smithsonian *Institution*

 ## Questions

1. What kinds of things can you see in a museum?
2. What is the Smithsonian Institution?
3. Why are museums like treasure chests?
4. What might be part of the Smithsonian one hundred years from now? How did you decide on your answer?

 ## Writing to Learn

THINK AND CHOOSE   Do you have favorite things you like to save? Draw a treasure chest. Show some of your favorite things in it.

WRITE   Choose one thing from your treasure chest. Write sentences that tell about it.

205

The Museum

I went to the museum,
it was filled with things to see,
there were rocks and gems
        and fossils
and a stuffed menagerie.

There were arrowheads and armor
and a mummy in a tomb,
I even saw a great blue whale
that took up one whole room.

I liked my afternoon there,
but I would have liked it more
if only they had let me pet
just one small dinosaur.

Jack Prelutsky

PLEASE DO NOT TOUCH

READING
TEACHER:
CHILDREN'S
CHOICE
1980

Maggie discovers a gift that says "hello" and "goodbye" at the same time.

Maggie
and the Goodbye Gift

written and illustrated by Sue and Jerry Milord

Hello there. My name is Margaret. But who I really am is Maggie.

One Friday night my dad came home from work and said, "Listen! Guess what's happened? My boss gave me that new job I asked for."

"That's wonderful!" my mom said.

Then my dad said to my mom, "There's one thing we hadn't counted on, though. We're being transferred."

My mom said, "Oh." And my brother Jack looked a little funny.

I didn't know what transferred meant at first, but it wasn't long before I found out. Being transferred means you have to leave the place where you live and move to another place far away where there is something called STRANGERS.

This made my mom and dad sad and my brother very unhappy. They didn't like having to leave Grandma and Grandpa and all our friends. But when you are transferred, that's what you have to do. Because you can't help it.

One day a big truck came and two strong men hopped out. They picked up all our furniture and carried it onto the truck. They made it look as easy as when I pick up the furniture in my doll house.

When we were ready to go, my mom's best friend Alice came to say her last goodbye. She gave us a gift. I thought, "Oh, how nice! This will make everybody feel much better."

When somebody gives me a gift, I always feel happy inside, and I open it up right away. But for some reason, my family only got sadder. And they didn't open it up at all. We just got into the car, waved goodbye, and drove away.

There were so many brand new things to see on the trip. And so many exciting places. It was fun! I wished everybody weren't so sad.

The next morning we got to our new house. After the big truck arrived, it didn't take long for the furniture to be moved inside.

At first everything was all jumbled up. When the rooms were put together again, the house looked fine. But we were not the same. We were on a street with all those STRANGERS.

"I miss Tommy and Stanley," said my brother.

"I miss Grandma and Grandpa and Alice," said my mom.

"I miss smiles and feeling happy inside," I said. Nobody heard me, though.

I had started to feel kind of sad myself, when I happened to go into the kitchen. There on the cabinet, sitting all by itself, was the goodbye gift. Everybody had forgotten it, and it looked lonesome. "Gifts are for opening," I said, and I opened it.

My Aunt Jennie had a thing that looked like this. I used to watch her use it. I decided to see if I could make this one work. Sure enough, I could. It made a nice buzzy sound, and I didn't feel sad anymore.

Later, when my mom walked into the kitchen, she got very upset. "Maggie!" she cried. "Look what you've done!"

My dad said, "Oh, Maggie! What are we going to do? We can't eat all of this by ourselves. It will spoil and have to be thrown away!"

Then Jack said, "Wow, Maggie! You've got enough stuff there to feed supper to everybody on both sides of the street."

My mom and dad looked at each other. Then my mom smiled for the first time all day and she said, "Well, why are we just standing around? We've got work to do."

Then my dad left the house. The goodbye gift had started to work magic.

My dad knocked on all the STRANGERS' doors. The STRANGERS laughed when they heard what the goodbye gift had done. And they promised to come over to our house for supper.

We got so busy making pies with all the pumpkin, and salad with all the beans, that we forgot to be sad anymore. There were lots of good things for everybody.

But the best thing was that the
magic goodbye gift had turned all
those STRANGERS into people just
like us. So we had friends again.

This all happened a long time ago last summer. It's winter now, and I have a friend named Milton who comes to play.

Milton lives next door, but he and his family will be moving soon. He says this makes his mother and father and sister very unhappy.

He asked me one day, "Maggie, what is a STRANGER?"

"I'm not sure," I told him. "But don't worry, Milton. I have something that works magic on STRANGERS."

"All you have to do is open it up and use it."

Reader's Response

Would you like to invite all those people to supper—as Maggie's dad did? Tell why or why not.

Writing a Post Card

Think about the stories you have read. Daniel gave his carved duck as a gift to Mr. Pettigrew. Johnny Appleseed planted apple seeds as a gift to his country. Aliki became a wonderful artist and a writer.

Now you can make a gift to give to someone. Your gift is a post card that tells about a story.

Prewriting

Think of a story you like. Why do you like it? Choose a person you would like to write a post card to and tell about the story.

Make the picture side of your post card. Draw a picture about your story on a piece of cardboard.

Dear Jenny,
I liked reading "The Train Set" because it is about Peter's birthday and the gifts that his family wants to buy for him. There is a surprise at the end of the story. Read it and find out what happens!
Your friend,
Mary

Jenny Showe
23 East First St.
Walnut, California
95038

Writing

On a sheet of paper, practice writing the message that will go on the other side of your post card. Write the title of your story. Write one important thing that happens in the story. Write why you liked the story.

Revising

Read your message aloud. Is the title of the story correct? Did you tell one important thing that happens in the story? Make changes in your post-card message if you need to.

Proofreading

Check your writing again. Make sure you have a capital letter at the beginning of each sentence and a period at the end. Did you underline the title?

Copy your story message carefully onto the back of your post card. Don't forget to sign your name.

Publishing

Write the name and address of the person who will get your post card. Give your post card to that person, or put on a stamp and mail it.

Sharing Stories

In this unit you read many good stories, such as the one about Johnny Appleseed. Together your group will pick another story in the unit that you would like to retell. Each of you will retell part of the story.

Start by agreeing on a story in this unit that you want to retell. Decide who will tell the name of the story and where it takes place. Then decide which one of you will tell the beginning of the story, the middle of the story, and the end of the story.

Here are some things to do while you work:

♦ Listen when someone else is talking.

♦ Take turns telling part of the story.

♦ Let others know when you like how they told their part of the story.

After you have told the story among yourselves, tell the story to another group.

BOOKS TO ENJOY

A Chair For My Mother by Vera B. Williams *(Greenwillow, 1982)* A family loses all it has in a fire and dreams of buying a comfortable chair.

The Giving Tree by Shel Silverstein *(Harper & Row, 1964)* This story tells about a special friendship between a boy and a tree and how they share the gift of giving as they grow older.

The Best Present Is Me by Janet Wolf *(Harper & Row, 1984)* A small girl cannot find her grandmother's birthday gift but learns she has a present after all!

Mr. Rabbit and the Lovely Present by Charlotte Zolotow *(Harper & Row, 1962)* A girl and a rabbit search for a birthday present.

HERE'S THE PLAN

*W*e need a plan to do many things.

How does a plan help make things happen?

THE OLD STAGE COACH,
*painting by Eastman Johnson,
American, c. 1850*

Too Many Babas

written and illustrated by Carolyn Croll

When Baba Edis and her friends cook together, the results are surprising.

Baba Edis lived in a little house at the end of town. One morning when she woke up, it was very cold.

"This is a good day to make some soup to warm my bones," Baba Edis said as she put on her dress and stockings.

She got out her big, old soup pot, filled it with water, and set it on the stove to boil. "Now let us see what I have," said Baba Edis.

There was a bone she had saved and a cup of beans, some carrots, celery, and a cabbage. As the soup began to boil, it filled the air with a wonderful smell.

Baba Basha, who was passing by, got a whiff of the good smell and stopped in. "What is that delicious smell?" called Baba Basha.

"Just some soup to warm my bones on this cold day," said Baba Edis. "Please have a bowl when it is ready."

225

"I think I will," said Baba Basha. Baba Basha took a taste. "It needs salt, dear," she said and put some salt into the pot. Then she tasted it again. "That's better," she said and sat down.

In a little while, a face showed up at the window. It was Baba Yetta. "Come in," called Baba Basha. "Baba Edis is making soup to warm her bones on this cold day and if you care to wait until it is ready, you can have a bowl yourself."

Baba Edis pulled up another chair. Baba
Yetta took a taste. "Hmmmmmm," she said.
"It needs something. I know! Pepper!" Baba
Yetta grabbed the pepper mill and gave it a good
many turns. "Wonderful!" she cried and sat
down with Baba Basha.

Soon the door opened. "Why, this looks like a party, and what is that delicious smell, Baba Edis?" It was Baba Molka on her way home from the marketplace.

"Please come in and join us," called Baba Basha and Baba Yetta together. "Baba Edis is making soup to warm her bones on this cold day and has asked us to have some when it is ready. You can have some, too."

Baba Edis went into her bedroom to get another chair. While she was gone, Baba Molka tasted the soup. "Hmmmmmm," she said and went to her basket and pulled out a plump garlic bulb. "A little garlic is just the thing to finish off this soup," she said and plopped in four cloves of garlic.

Baba Edis got out the bowls and spoons. Then she put some dark bread in a basket on the table. After a while Baba Basha went to the soup pot to taste. "Hmmmmmmmm," she said. "Just a dash more salt and it will be just right."

"Nearly ready?" asked Baba Yetta. She lifted the lid and took a whiff. "It doesn't smell spicy enough," she said and grabbed the pepper mill.

"Let me give it a stir," Baba Molka said and took the spoon from Baba Yetta. "It looks a little thin," said Baba Molka. "Another clove or two of garlic will make it much better."

"I think the soup is ready," said Baba Edis. "I hope you are all hungry." She put the soup into the bowls and passed them to her friends.

"It looks delicious," said Baba Basha.

"It smells delicious," said Baba Yetta and Baba Molka. They all sat down at the table.

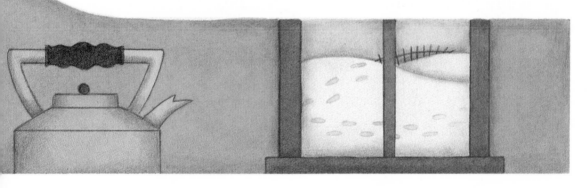

Baba Edis said, "I think too many cooks
spoiled my soup. This is terrible, terrible soup.
Now all we have for dinner is bread and water."

"We are very sorry, Baba Edis," said Baba
Basha.

"I wish there was a way to start again,"
said Baba Yetta.

"Wait!" said Baba Molka. She reached for her basket. "I have a cabbage and some celery and beans and carrots. If we are going to help make soup, then this time we need a plan. Each of us will do one part."

"I'll wash out the pot and put water on to boil," said Baba Basha.

"I'll wash the cabbage, the celery, the beans, and the carrots," said Baba Yetta.

"And I'll chop them up," said Baba Molka.

They all got to work. Soon the soup was boiling. Baba Edis was feeling much better now. She lifted the lid and took a taste.

"Only I will add the salt and pepper and garlic," she said. She measured them out. Then she tasted the soup again.

When the soup was ready, Baba Basha, Baba Yetta, Baba Molka, and Baba Edis were so hungry they each had two bowls full. When they were finished, Baba Basha cleared the table. Baba Yetta washed the dishes. Baba Molka dried the dishes. And Baba Edis put them away. Then they all said good night.

 ## Reader's Response

Do you think too many cooks can spoil a pot of soup? Tell why or why not.

Too Many Babas

Questions

1. Why did Baba Edis's friends want to add things to the soup?
2. What did each Baba add to the soup?
3. Why was the first pot of soup terrible?
4. Why did the Babas decide they needed a plan to make soup?
5. What did Baba Edis and her friends think of the second pot of soup? What clues in the story helped you know this?

Writing to Learn

THINK AND DECIDE   The Babas put many kinds of food into their soup. What foods would you put into your own pot of soup? Draw a picture of your pot of soup and the foods you would put into it.

WRITE   Name your soup and write a recipe. Tell how to make your soup.

233

Helping

by Shel Silverstein

Agatha Fry, she made a pie
And Christopher John helped bake it.
Christopher John, he mowed the lawn,
And Agatha Fry helped rake it.
Zachary Zugg took out the rug,
And Jennifer Joy helped shake it.
And Jennifer Joy, she made a toy,
And Zachary Zugg helped break it.

And some kind of help
Is the kind of help
That helping's all about.
And some kind of help
Is the kind of help
We all can do without.

A Strategy for Thinking:

Asking Why

How can you better understand what you read? One way is to ask *why*.

Learning the Strategy

In the article about the Smithsonian Institution, the author said:

Museums are just like treasure chests.

When you read that, did you ask yourself, "Why are museums like treasure chests"?

In a story about Johnny Appleseed, you learned that Johnny did not go west in a covered wagon. He walked in his bare feet.

Did you ask why? Did you ask yourself why Johnny went west in his bare feet?

At the end of "Daniel's Duck," you learned that Daniel held the duck a little longer. Then he gave it to Henry Pettigrew.

Why did Daniel hold the duck a little longer? Why did he give it to Henry Pettigrew? Did you wonder? Did you ask why?

Many times the author does not give an answer to *why* questions. Then you have to work out the answer yourself. Thinking of your own answers to *why* questions can be fun.

If you ask why and try to answer, you may better understand what you read.

Using the Strategy

Look back at the story "Too Many Babas." Find two places where you would like to ask why something happened. Discuss your questions and your answers. Did you understand more by asking and answering your *why* questions?

Applying the Strategy to the Next Selection

The next selection you will read is "Check It Out." At several points you will have the chance to ask and answer *why* questions.

◆◆◆   The writing connection can be found on page 253.

Check It Out!

written and illustrated by Gail Gibbons

Libraries are filled with books and information and much much more.

There are small libraries and there are big libraries.

The biggest library in the United States is the Library of Congress in Washington, D. C. A copy of most of the books printed in this country is kept there—millions and millions of books.

238

No matter what its size, a library is filled with books and information. The word *library* comes from the Latin word for book—*liber*.

Before there were books, words were printed by hand on tablets of clay or on scrolls. Later, people lettered whole books by hand. This lettering took a long time. The first libraries had only hand-lettered books.

Now libraries have printed books. Printing presses can print thousands of books in a short time. ◄◈►

◄◈►
Why are there different kinds of libraries?

239

There are different kinds of libraries. Public libraries and school libraries have books and information about everything you need to know. Other libraries have special collections of books about only one or two things such as horses or plants.

Most libraries have all kinds of books.

Finding the book you want takes practice. Libraries are organized in different ways. If you are looking for a book, you can ask a librarian to help you. You can use the card catalog, a book catalog, or a computer.

A book can be read at the library, or it can be checked out and taken home. To keep track of who has the books, libraries use either a computer, a library card, or sometimes just your name. ◄◆►

When books are returned, they are checked in and placed back on the shelves for other people to read.

Librarians are always ready to help you find a good book to read, and they are there to answer questions.

◄◆► **Why do libraries use computers?**

Librarians collect books and information from many places. They read new books and listen to ideas from other people. They also find books in catalogs.

Sometimes people give books to the library. Some people also give their time to help keep the library running smoothly. ◄◆►

◄◆►
Why do some people give books to the library?

Many public libraries have helpers called Friends of the Library. The Friends of the Library help with special things, such as making money to buy more books.

Public libraries and school libraries have different parts for different people. Libraries also have special books for people who have handicaps.

Libraries will sometimes take books to people who cannot get to the library building. In some places there are libraries on wheels, called bookmobiles. Bookmobiles visit people who don't have a library nearby. ◄◆►

◄◆►

Why do some libraries have bookmobiles?

Besides books, the library has records, tapes, and computers. Some libraries have puzzles and toys, newspapers, maps, globes, and much more.

Many things take place at the library. There may be puppet shows, movies, story hours, summer reading classes, and even art classes.

  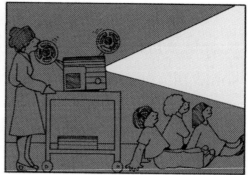

Often there are special exhibits. Authors and artists may come to the library to talk about their work.

The library is a place to learn about new things, to find the answers to questions, and most important, to enjoy the fun of reading!

◆ LIBRARY LINK ◆

You can find many books by Gail Gibbons in the library. Look for The Magnificent Morris Mouse Clubhouse *and* The Post Office Book.

 Reader's Response

Does this selection make you more interested in libraries? Why or why not?

Check It Out!

Questions

1. What things are kept in a library?
2. What kinds of things can you do at a library?
3. Can you think of another good title for this selection? When you were choosing your title, what titles did you think of?
4. What did you learn from reading this selection?

Writing to Learn

THINK AND DISCOVER Pretend you are a book in a library. Draw your cover. Write the name of your book and the author.

WRITE Write two sentences about the stories in your book.

A lot of people help Nick at his new school.
Now Nick wants to find a way to help them.

Nick Joins In

written and illustrated by Joe Lasker

Nick was worried. He didn't know what to
expect. Soon he would be going to a new
school. No longer would a teacher visit his
home.

Nick's mother had told him, "You'll be
going to school, the way other children do.
Before you start, we'll visit your school. We'll
meet your new teacher and her aide."

Nick, who couldn't walk or run, was worried. "How will I go up and down the stairs?" he thought. "Will I be as smart as the other children?"

Nick asked his parents many questions. "How can I go to school in my wheelchair?" he asked. "What if the kids don't like me? Will there be anyone else who can't walk?"

His mother said, "Nick, at first the other children will look at you and ask questions."

"After a while you'll get used to each other and be friends," his father said. Nick felt a little better.

The school was getting ready for Nick. The workers built a ramp for his wheelchair.

A special desk was put in Mrs. Becker's classroom. She told her children about Nick and his wheelchair.

When Nick was dropped off at his school, a teacher's aide met him and said, "We hope you like our school, Nick." Then she pushed Nick up the new ramp and into a long hall.

Nick had never been with so many boys and girls. A bell rang and the children went into their classrooms.

The aide wheeled Nick into his classroom. Everyone looked at him. Mrs. Becker smiled. "We're glad you're here," she said.

Nick met all the boys and girls. Nick wondered if he would remember their names. He stared at the floor, wishing he were home.

No one spoke. Then Mrs. Becker said, "Nick, I think the children would like to ask you some questions. Is that all right?"

Nick nodded, still looking down.

Rachel asked the first question. "Why do you have to use a wheelchair?"

"Because I can't walk," Nick said, not looking at her.

"Why can't you walk?" asked Nina.

"Because my legs don't grow right."

"Why is that?" asked Timmie.

Nick looked at him and said, "I was born that way."

Cindy pointed to the braces on Nick's legs. "Why do you wear those?" she said.

"They help me stand," Nick told her.

"All right, boys and girls," said Mrs. Becker, "it's time to begin our work."

Mrs. Becker helped Nick to his new desk. Then it was his turn to look around.

Nick looked at all the children. He looked at his teacher and at the bright pictures on the walls. He didn't feel so afraid anymore. He thought he might like school.

Days went by. Nick and the other children grew used to each other. Without being asked, people helped Nick.

Nick helped people, too. Sometimes he helped the gym teacher open windows with the long window pole.

Nick also made friends. One of them was Timmie. He couldn't run like Timmie, but he moved fast.

What Nick wished for most was to play ball at recess like the others. How fast and high they ran and jumped! To Nick, that was like flying.

One afternoon there was a ball game. Higher and higher the ball went, until it landed on the roof of the gym. The ball rolled to the edge of the roof, but instead of dropping down, it got stuck in the rain gutter. All the children groaned.

Timmie threw a basketball to hit the ball out of the gutter. But the ball didn't move.

Nina threw a stone, but that didn't help.

"Oh, we'll never finish our game," said Timmie.

Nick had an idea. He went into the gym and past the tall gym windows, straight to where the window pole was. He took the pole and wheeled back outside.

Nina saw Nick coming. "Nick to the rescue," she shouted. "In the nick of time!"

"Excuse me, please," said Nick. He stopped under the gutter and looked up. He lifted up the pole and poked the ball. Down it dropped.

"Hooray for Nick!" everyone cheered.

Nick felt he was flying.

♦ LIBRARY LINK ♦

Joe Lasker has written many books you will enjoy. Look in the library for He's My Brother *and* Tales of a Seadog Family.

Reader's Response

What things would you do with Nick if he came to your home to play?

Nick Joins In

 Questions

1. Why was Nick worried about school?
2. If Nick had not been in a wheelchair, would he still have been afraid of starting school? What makes you think so?
3. Why did the children want to ask Nick questions about his handicap?
4. Nick felt he was "flying" after he got the ball free. What does this mean?

 Writing to Learn

THINK AND DECIDE Think about Nick's first day at school. How did he feel? Why do you think he felt that way?

Think About what the story says about Nick's first day.
Think About what you already know about meeting someone new.

WRITE Write a sentence. Tell why Nick felt the way he did on his first day.

253

Comprehension:

Main Idea and Supporting Details

Read this paragraph from "Check It Out."

There are different kinds of libraries. Public libraries and school libraries have books and information about everything you need to know.

Do you remember what the topic of a paragraph is? The *topic* is one or two words that tell what the paragraph is about. The topic of the paragraph is *libraries*.

The *main idea* is a sentence that tells what the paragraph says about the topic.

Read the paragraph again. The first sentence, "There are different kinds of libraries," is the main idea of the paragraph. After you read the first sentence, you know that the paragraph is about different kinds of libraries.

The main idea is often in the beginning of a paragraph. But sometimes it's at the end.

The second sentence tells about different kinds of libraries: public libraries and school libraries. This sentence gives *details* about the main idea.

Using What You Have Learned

Read this paragraph and answer the questions.

Forest fires are dangerous. Forest fires can hurt animals. Many trees can be destroyed, too. People can also be hurt by forest fires.

1. Write the sentence that tells the main idea.
2. Which sentences give details about the main idea?

As You Read

The next article you will read is called "The Biggest Living Thing." As you read, look for the main idea in a paragraph.

The
BIGGEST
Living Thing

by Caroline Arnold

One plant is taller than the Statue of Liberty and bigger than any other living thing!

Who Found the Giant Sequoias?

Giant sequoia (si kwoi′ə) trees grow in the Sierra Nevada mountains in California. The biggest sequoia tree of all grows in Sequoia National Park. It is 272 feet tall.

Native Americans knew about the giant trees, but for a long time no one else did. Then in 1848 people found gold in California. Men came from all over to look for gold. They walked, rode horses, and came in covered wagons. They became gold miners. The miners lived in camps in the Sierra Nevada mountains.

In 1852, Augustus T. Dowd, who worked at a camp, went into the forest to hunt for food. He made an amazing discovery. He found a giant sequoia tree.

It grew high into the sky and was bigger than anything he had ever seen. He didn't know it yet, but it was the biggest tree in the world.

Augustus Dowd rushed back to camp. He told everyone what he had seen. They all laughed.

"You are joking!" they said. "There is no such thing as a tree that big." No one believed him.

No one would go into the forest to look, so Augustus Dowd decided to trick the miners. He waited a few days. Then he rushed back again from the forest.

This time he said, "Come quickly! I killed a big bear. Help me bring it back!"

Everyone ran after him to see the big bear. Augustus Dowd led the miners through the forest.

"Where is the bear?" they asked.

"We will see it soon," he said.

Just then they saw the giant sequoia tree. Everyone stopped, amazed.

"See," said Augustus Dowd. "There is no bear, but there really is a giant tree."

Soon many people were coming to see the giant trees. It wasn't long before people around the world knew about the giant sequoias.

People came to look at the sequoias. Some people came to cut them down. Everyone wanted to know more about the giant sequoias. How old were they? How did they grow to be so big?

The stumps of the giant sequoias were huge. One was so big, it was used for a dance floor.

On each stump there were rings. Each year a tree grows two rings—a light ring in the spring and a dark ring in the summer. People counted the rings on each stump. Then they knew how old the tree had been. One tree had 3,200 pairs of rings. It was 3,200 years old!

How Do the Giant Sequoias Grow?

Each sequoia tree grows from a very small seed. The seed grows inside a pine cone. When it is ripe, the seed falls to the earth. The rain makes it damp. The sun makes it warm. Then it grows.

At first a sequoia looks like other pine trees. When it is about seventy-five years old, it may be over one hundred feet tall. Then the trunk becomes bare at the bottom. The branches stick out like arms at the top. The bark becomes dark red. It begins to look like a giant sequoia.

The giant sequoia is like most plants. It needs the sun, rain, and soil to grow. But it needs one more thing, too: fire! A forest fire is a terrible thing, but sometimes a small fire can help the sequoias.

5 years   25 years   75 years

Large giant sequoia trees are not usually hurt by fire because they are so strong. They have thick bark that does not burn easily.

| 1,000 years | 2,000 years | 3,000 years |

How Does Fire Help?

Fire helps the giant sequoias in many ways. Fire helps to clear the ground for the sequoia seeds. They must fall on bare soil to grow. Sometimes the ground is covered with leaves and branches. Then the seeds get lost before they reach the soil. Fire burns up the leaves and branches on the forest floor.

Fire also helps the seeds come out of their cones. Usually the seeds are held tightly inside the cones. Forest fires heat up the air. This makes the cones dry out. Then they open up. The seeds fall down onto the soil.

Fires also clear out the sequoia groves. The fire kills other kinds of trees and clears out small sequoia trees. This gives the big trees room to grow even bigger.

Most giant sequoia trees do not get sick and die, but they can fall over. Sometimes their roots are not strong enough to hold them up.

A man named Hale Tharp once made his home in the hollow trunk of a fallen tree. The room inside that tree is fifty-six feet long. It is eight feet tall at one end and four feet tall at the other end!

Can You Still See the Giant Sequoias?

People no longer cut down the big trees. Now the trees are protected so that everyone can see them. Many people visit the sequoia trees every year.

The giant sequoia is a very special tree. It is tall. It is beautiful. It is the biggest living thing.

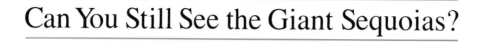

◆ LIBRARY LINK ◆

If you would like to learn more about forests and trees, read How the Forest Grew *by William Jaspersohn.*

Reader's Response

Do you think it is important to save and protect the giant sequoias? Why?

The BIGGEST Living Thing

Questions

1. How is a sequoia like other plants? How is it different? How did you know?
2. What do a tree's rings tell about a tree?
3. Why do you think so many people visit the giant sequoias?
4. What is the main idea of this story? What are some details that tell about the main idea?

Writing to Learn

THINK AND REMEMBER Draw a giant sequoia on your paper. Use the branches of your tree as a resting place for facts.

WRITE Write three interesting facts on your sequoia tree.

Harlequin wants to go to the carnival. His friends have a plan to help him.

HARLEQUIN
and the Gift of
Many Colors

by Remy Charlip and Burton Supree
Paintings by Remy Charlip
Story adapted by José Rivera

Commercial use of this story is prohibited without written permission of the authors.

Players

Narrator	Columbine
Isabella	Zany
Punch	Harlequin
Pierot	Townspeople

266

Act One

Narrator: This morning, everyone in town is getting ready for the great Carnival. Some are setting up tables where sweets and food and drink will be sold. Others are setting up games. (Isabella, Columbine, Pierot, Punch, *and* Zany *enter*.)

Isabella: I can't wait for tonight's Carnival.

Punch: I hear there are going to be lots of games and delicious food.

Pierot: And there will be dancing and singing.

Columbine: Best of all, everyone will be wearing beautiful new costumes!

Zany: By the way, where is Harlequin? He is always the first one out.

Punch: I haven't seen him all morning.

Pierot: Maybe his mother won't let him come out, or maybe he is sick.

Narrator: The children rush to Harlequin's house.

Act Two

Narrator: Harlequin is looking out the window of his house at the busy street. (*The children enter.*)

Zany: Harlequin, are you all right? Why don't you come down to the square?

Isabella: Harlequin, come on out. It's the day of the big Carnival!

Punch: My father says I can stay up as long as I want to!

Columbine: Come on, Harlequin! Let's go and watch the dancers practicing!

Narrator: Harlequin is quiet and sad, but he goes out with his friends. They begin walking to the square.

Zany: I'm going to wear a costume with a mask! No one will know it's me.

Pierot: My costume is yellow like the sun!

Punch: Mine is made of thick cloth as black as the night!

Columbine: Wait until you see mine. It's purple!

Isabella: And I've got the biggest green buttons you've ever seen!

(*The children laugh.*)

Pierot: What are you going to wear tonight, Harlequin?

Harlequin: Well . . . I'll wear my blanket as a cape.

Columbine: Don't be silly. What are you *really* going to wear tonight?

Harlequin: Nothing. I'm not even going to the Carnival. (Harlequin *runs away*.)

Isabella: Not coming? How can that be?

Zany: Maybe he is teasing us.

Pierot: I think I know why he isn't coming. He doesn't have a new costume to wear.

Zany: But Harlequin *must* go to the Carnival!

Columbine: What can we do? We must help!

Punch: I know! I have an idea. My coat doesn't need to be so long. I can cut some off and give it to Harlequin.

Pierot: Yes! My dress doesn't have to be so long. I can give him some of my cloth.

Punch: If we each give him a piece of cloth, he will have enough for a whole costume.

Columbine: Let's go and get the cloth right now.

Isabella: Then we'll meet at Harlequin's house.

Act Three

Narrator: The sun is high in the sky as they meet at Harlequin's house. Each one has a gift of cloth.

(Isabella *taps on* Harlequin's *door.* Harlequin *opens the door, and the children enter.* Harlequin *looks surprised.*)

Isabella: These pieces of cloth from our costumes are for you! We thought maybe you could use them.

Narrator: As they give him their pieces of cloth, they see that each piece is a different shape and color. None of the pieces match. They look like a pile of rags.

Harlequin: Thank you.

Narrator: The children are afraid they have made Harlequin even sadder than before.

Punch: (*sadly*) We hope you can come tonight, Harlequin. Goodbye.

(*The children leave.*)

Harlequin: My friends have tried to help, but what can I do with these? They don't even match. Not one piece is big enough for even a sleeve. I'm not going out until the Carnival is over.

(Harlequin *throws the rags up in the air, but one piece sticks to* Harlequin.)

Narrator: Harlequin looks at the piece, and then he has an idea.

Harlequin: If I put all these scraps onto my old suit, could I make a costume? I can! It will be beautiful, but it will take hours of work. I must rush to finish it by tonight.

(Harlequin *gets his old suit and begins sewing
    with his back to the audience*.)

Narrator: Harlequin covers the suit with scraps
    of cloth. Then he begins to sew them onto
    the suit. Hours and hours pass. Harlequin
    keeps working as the night comes. Moonlight
    streams into his room. He hears music from
    far away. The Carnival is beginning.

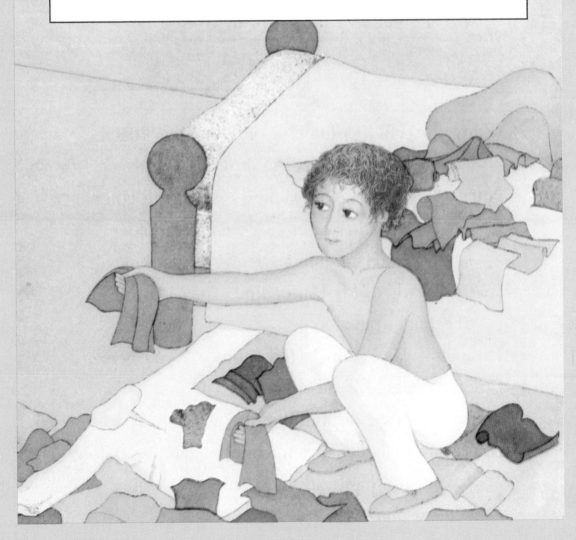

Harlequin: It's finished! (Harlequin *turns around to face the audience*.)

Narrator: What a beautiful costume Harlequin has made from patches of every color! He puts on the costume and spins around and around, as bright as a butterfly.

Harlequin: It's wonderful! (Harlequin *puts on a hat and mask, and runs out of the house*.)

Act Four

(Zany, Isabella, Columbine, Pierot, *and* Punch *enter. All are wearing costumes*.)

Narrator: The town square is wild with color. All the world seems to be dancing and singing. Harlequin's friends are looking everywhere for Harlequin. They hope that he might have come.

Isabella: Harlequin! Harlequin, are you here?

Punch: Where is he?

Pierot: Maybe he didn't come after all.

Narrator: Suddenly, someone is standing before them in an amazing costume. (Harlequin *enters dancing*.)

Zany: Look! What a costume!

Pierot: I've never seen anything so beautiful!

Punch: Who is it? Where is he from?

Isabella: No one knows.

Narrator: As Harlequin dances, all the colors he wears shine in the light like jewels.

Zany: Wait! That piece of blue is mine!

Columbine: That purple piece is from my dress!

Pierot: That must be Harlequin!

Isabella: It *is* Harlequin!

Narrator: ''Harlequin! Harlequin!'' The children cheer and dance and hug Harlequin.

Harlequin: I am the happiest of all tonight, for I am clothed in the love of my friends.

The End

◆ LIBRARY LINK ◆

Plays are fun to read and to act out. Your class might also enjoy The Red Shoes *by Hans Christian Andersen.*

Reader's Response

Would you like to have friends like Harlequin's friends? Tell why.

HARLEQUIN
and the Gift of Many Colors

 Questions

1. Why didn't Harlequin want to go to the carnival?
2. What did Harlequin's friends do to help Harlequin?
3. What words would you use to describe Harlequin's friends?
4. What did Harlequin mean when he said, "I am clothed in the love of my friends"? How did you figure out what it meant?

 Writing to Learn

THINK AND INVENT Harlequin's suit of many colors became a gift of friendship. You can make a gift like Harlequin's. Draw a shape and lines with a dark crayon. Color each part a different color.

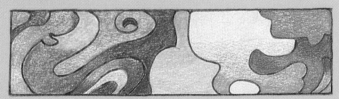

WRITE Give your picture to a friend. Write to tell why it is fun to give a gift.

Literature:

Learning About Characters

Characters are the people, the animals, and the make-believe creatures in a story. We learn about a character from what the writer tells us and what the character says and does. Read these sentences from "Nick Joins In."

Nick helped people, too. Sometimes he helped the gym teacher open windows with the long window pole.

Nick also made friends. One of them was Timmie. He couldn't run like Timmie, but he moved fast.

You learned what Nick was like by reading the words the writer used to describe him.

Using Story Clues

Sometimes you must use clues in a story to tell what the characters are like. Read these sentences from "Harlequin and the Gift of Many Colors."

Zany: But Harlequin *must* go to the Carnival! . . .

Punch: I know! I have an idea. My coat doesn't need to be so long. I can cut some off and give it to Harlequin.

Pierot: Yes! My dress doesn't have to be so long. I can give him some of my cloth.

We can tell from what Harlequin's friends say and do that they care about him. They are kind and thoughtful.

Read and Enjoy

As you read the next story, "Frederick," think of what Frederick is like. Look for clues in the story.

CALDECOTT
HONOR
1968

In this story, all the little mice work hard gathering food, except for Frederick. He has a different plan.

Frederick

written and illustrated
by Leo Lionni

All along the meadow where the cows grazed and the horses ran, there was an old stone wall. In that wall, not far from the barn and the granary, a chatty family of field mice had their home.

But the farmers had moved away. The barn was abandoned and the granary stood empty. And since winter was not far off, the little mice began to gather corn and nuts and wheat and straw. They all worked day and night. All—except Frederick.

"Frederick, why don't you work?"
they asked.

"I *do* work," said Frederick.

"I gather sun rays for the cold dark
winter days."

And when they saw Frederick sitting
there, staring at the meadow, they said, "And
now, Frederick?"

"I gather colors," answered Frederick
simply. "For winter is gray."

And once Frederick seemed half asleep. "Are you dreaming, Frederick?" they asked.

But Frederick said, "Oh no, I am gathering words. For the winter days are long and many, and we'll run out of things to say."

The winter days came, and when the first snow fell, the five little field mice took to their hideout in the stones. In the beginning there was lots to eat, and the mice told stories of foolish foxes and silly cats. They were a happy family.

But little by little they had nibbled up most of the nuts and berries, the straw was gone, and the corn was only a memory. It was cold in the wall and no one felt like chatting.

Then the mice remembered what Frederick had said about sunrays and colors and words. "What about *your* supplies, Frederick?" they asked.

"Close your eyes," said Frederick, as he climbed onto a big stone. "Now I send you the rays of the sun. Do you feel how their golden glow . . ."

And as Frederick spoke of the sun the four little mice began to feel warmer. Was it Frederick's voice? Was it magic?

"And how about the colors, Frederick?" they asked anxiously.

290

"Close your eyes again," Frederick said. And when he told them of the blue periwinkles, the red poppies in the yellow wheat, and the green leaves of the berry bush, they saw the colors as clearly as if they had been painted in their minds.

"And the words, Frederick?"

Frederick cleared his throat, waited a
moment, and then, as if from a stage, he said:

"Who scatters snowflakes? Who melts the ice?
Who spoils the weather? Who makes it nice?
Who grows the four-leaf clovers in June?
Who dims the daylight? Who lights the moon?

Four little field mice who live in the sky.
Four little field mice . . . like you and I.

One is the Springmouse who turns on the showers.
Then comes the Summer who paints in the flowers.
The Fallmouse is next with walnuts and wheat.
And Winter is last . . . with little cold feet.

Aren't we lucky the seasons are four?
Think of a year with one less . . . or one more!"

When Frederick had finished, they all
clapped. "But Frederick," they said, "you are
a poet!"

Frederick blushed, took a bow, and said
shyly, "I know it."

◆ LIBRARY LINK ◆

*You will enjoy reading other books by
Leo Lionni. Look in the library for* Alexander
and the Wind-up Mouse *and* Little Blue and
Little Yellow.

 Reader's Response

Do you think Frederick had a good way
of getting ready for winter? Tell why.

Writing a Plan

People often need plans to do things well. Nick had a plan to get the ball out of the gutter. Baba Edis and her friends needed a plan to make good soup.

You can write plans for a birthday party for a story character in this unit.

Prewriting

Choose a character from one of the stories. Plan a birthday party. Would you play games?

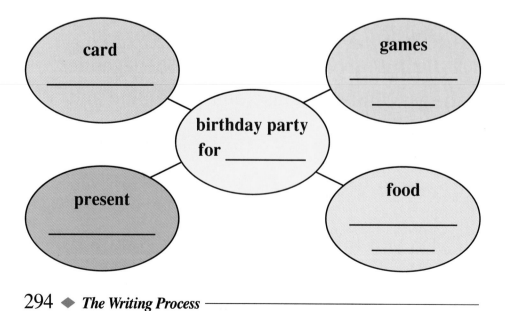

Writing

Write your plans for the party. Use the words *first, next, then,* and *last* to help you write about what will happen.

Revising

Ask someone to read your plans. Ask if your plans are clear. Did you remember to use the words *first, next, then,* and *last?*

Proofreading

Read your plan. Do your sentences begin with a capital letter? Do they end with a period?

Make a final copy of your plan. Use your best handwriting.

Publishing

Make a ''Happy Birthday'' book. Use everyone's plans.

Planning Lunch

A plan helped Baba Edis make better soup. Your group can work together to plan and make a picture of a nice lunch.

As you work, be sure to do these things to help your group work well:

- ◆ Listen when other people talk.
- ◆ Make sure people take turns.
- ◆ Make a list of everyone's favorite foods.
- ◆ Help everyone finish on time.

Before you begin, be sure you have a paper plate, crayons, and paper. Then talk together about what you like to eat and drink for lunch. Take turns naming your favorite foods.   Write a list of ideas.

Decide together who will draw or cut out a picture of each kind of food.   When you have finished, paste all of the pictures on a paper plate.

Share your plan: Select one person to describe your lunch to another group.

Where Does the Teacher Live? by Paula Feder *(Dutton, 1979)* A second-grade class plays detective to find out where their teacher lives.

Brave Irene by William Steig *(Farrar, Straus & Giroux, 1986)* When her mother is ill, Irene braves a wintry evening to take a gown to the duchess.

Send Wendell by Genevieve Gray *(McGraw-Hill, 1974)* Everyone in Wendell's family says "Send Wendell" when there is a job to be done.

The One Hundred Year Old Cactus by Anita Holmes *(Four Winds Press, 1983)* You will see how long it takes the giant saguaro cactus to grow.

GLOSSARY

Full pronunciation key* The pronunciation of each word is shown just after the word, in this way: **abbreviate** (ə brē′vē āt).

The letters and signs used are pronounced as in the words below.

The mark **′** is placed after a syllable with primary or heavy accent as in the example above.

The mark **′** after a syllable shows a secondary or lighter accent, as in **abbreviation** (ə brē′vē ā′shən).

SYMBOL	KEY WORDS	SYMBOL	KEY WORDS	SYMBOL	KEY WORDS
a	ask, fat	u	up, cut	r	red, dear
ā	ape, date	ʉr	fur, fern	s	sell, pass
ä	car, father			t	top, hat
		ə	**a** in ago	v	vat, have
e	elf, ten		**e** in agent	w	will, always
er	berry, care		**e** in father	y	yet, yard
ē	even, meet		**i** in unity	z	zebra, haze
			o in collect		
i	is, hit		**u** in focus	ch	chin, arch
ir	mirror, here			ŋ	ring, singer
ī	ice, fire	b	bed, dub	sh	she, dash
		d	did, had	th	thin, truth
o	lot, pond	f	fall, off	*th*	then, father
ō	open, go	g	get, dog	zh	**s** in pleasure
ô	law, horn	h	he, ahead		
oi	oil, point	j	joy, jump	′	as in (ā′b′l)
oo	look, pull	k	kill, bake		
o͞o	ooze, tool	l	let, ball		
yoo	unite, cure	m	met, trim		
yo͞o	cute, few	n	not, ton		
ou	out, crowd	p	put, tap		

*Pronunciation key and respellings adapted from *Webster's New World Dictionary, Basic School Edition,* Copyright © 1983 by Simon & Schuster, Inc. Reprinted by permission.

A

act (akt) one of the main parts of a play: "The first *act* takes place in a park."

a·do·be (ə dō′bē) brick made of sun-dried clay: "The house was made of *adobe*."

a·dults (ə dults′ *or* ad′ults) **1.** grown-ups. **2.** men or women who are grown up: "The children stood in front of the *adults*."

a·fraid (ə frād′) frightened: "They are *afraid* of the dark."

a·gainst (ə genst′) **1.** opposite or opposed to. **2.** touched, next to: "The dog rubbed *against* my leg."

a·head (ə hed′) in the front or to the front: "Katie was *ahead* of me in line."

aide (ād) an assistant or helper: "The teacher's *aide* checked the papers."

a·long (ə lông′) on or beside: "Walk *along* the side of the road."

al·though (ôl *th*ō′) **1.** even if. **2.** in spite of the fact that: "He fell *although* he was careful."

an·gry (aṅg′grē) feeling or showing anger: "My brother made me *angry*."

an·swer (an′sər) a reply to a question: "Your *answer* to the question is correct."

a·part·ment (ə pärt′mənt) a group of rooms in a building: "Our *apartment* is on the third floor."

ap·ple (ap″l) a round fruit with red, yellow, or green skin and small seeds: "An *apple* is sweet and crunchy."

art (ärt) painting, drawing, or sculpture: "John made two paintings in *art* class."

art·ist (är′tist) a person who creates art: "The *artist* made the painting."

adobe

against

apples

barre

au·di·ence (ô′dē əns) a group of people gathered together to hear or see a show: "The *audience* was very quiet."

au·thors (ô′thərz) people who write things such as books or stories: "The *authors* told us how they got their story ideas."

av·a·lanche (av′ ə lanch) large mass of snow or rocks sliding very fast down a mountain: "The *avalanche* covered the mountain road."

B

back·ward (bak′wərd) toward the back; behind: "He looked *backward* as he walked."

barre (bär) French word for a railing used by ballet dancers: "She held onto the *barre* as she stretched her leg."

baseball team

base·ball (bās′bôl) **1.** a game played using a ball and bat by two teams of nine players each: "Pedro watched his sister play *baseball*." **2.** the ball used in the game.

be·low (bi lō′) in or to a lower place: "The paper was *below* the desk."

be·side (bi sīd′) **1.** by or next to. **2.** upset: "She was *beside* herself with worry."

be·tween (bi twēn′) **1.** in the middle of or connecting: "I stood *between* Pat and Sue."

between

block (blok) **1.** a thick piece of flat material. **2.** land with buildings on it separated from other land by streets: "The parade was on our *block*."

boil (boil) to heat a liquid until it bubbles and becomes steam: "I need to *boil* water for gravy."

book·mo·biles (book′mō bēlz) traveling libraries in vans that go to places where there are no libraries: "The *bookmobiles* come to our town on Tuesday."

bought (bôt) have gotten something by paying for it: "I *bought* new sneakers at the store."

bowls (bōlz) deep, round dishes: "Dad washed the soup *bowls*."

brave (brāv) **1.** not afraid: "Ben was *brave* during the storm." **2.** a North American Indian warrior.

built (bilt) constructed; made by putting together parts or materials: "He *built* the house with sticks."

burn·ing (bʉrn′iŋ) giving off light: "The candle was *burning* for a long time."

bus·y (biz′ē) active; at work: "The teacher was *busy*."

but·ter·fly (but′ər flī) an insect with a thin body and wide wings: "The *butterfly* had colorful wings."

but·tons (but′ənz) small disks sewed to clothing, used as fasteners when pushed through the buttonholes: "The *buttons* on the shirt held it tightly closed."

buy (bī) get something by paying money: "I wanted to *buy* the doll."

a fat	ɔi oil	ch chin
ā ape	๐๐ look	sh she
ä car, father	ōō tool	th thin
e ten	๐u out	*th* then
er care	u up	zh leisure
ē even	ʉr fur	n̂g ring
i hit		
ir here	ə = a *in* ago	
ī bite, fire	e *in* agent	
o lot	i *in* unity	
ō go	o *in* collect	
ô law, horn	u *in* focus	

butterfly

C

cab·bage (kab′ij) a vegetable with thick leaves folded tightly over one another: "We grow *cabbage* in our garden."

cab·in (kab′in) a small house built in a simple way: "She lives in a log *cabin*."

ca·boose (kə bōōs′) usually the last car on a freight train: "The train had a red *caboose*."

card cat·a·log (kärd kat″l ôg) a card file in alphabetical order with a complete list of books in a library: "The *card catalog* told me where to find books about goldfish."

cabbage

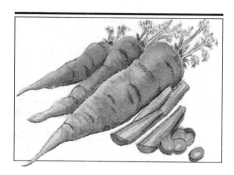

carrots

celery

climb

car·ni·val (kär′nə v′l) a party with parades, games, food, and dancing: "Our town has a *carnival* once each year."

car·ried (kar′ēd) taken from one place to another: "The train *carried* my friends to their new home."

car·rots (kar′əts) plants with long orange roots eaten as vegetables: "The *carrots* were ready to be pulled."

carve ((kärv) make by cutting: "He used the knife to *carve* the jack-o-lantern."

carv·ings (kär′vingz) carved figures: "*Carvings* are works of art made by cutting."

cel·e·ry (sel′ər ē) a plant whose long, crisp stalks are eaten as a vegetable: "*Celery* makes a good snack."

cer·tain·ly (surt″n lē) surely; without any doubt: "I will *certainly* come to see you."

cheer·ful (chir′fəl) glad; joyful: "I was *cheerful* at the party."

child (chīld) **1.** a young boy or girl. **2.** a son or daughter: "I am my mother's *child.*"

chil·dren (chil′drən) young boys and girls: "The *children* go to school."

chim·ney (chim′nē) a pipe or shaft going up through a roof to carry off smoke from a fire: "The smoke went up the *chimney.*"

ci·der (sī′dər) juice made from pressed apples: "We drank *cider* with our lunch."

class (klas) **1.** a group of people or things that are alike in some ways. **2.** a group of students that meet together: "My dance *class* meets on Saturday mornings."

climb (klīm) go up or down using feet and sometimes hands: "I like to *climb* trees."

clos·et (kloz′it) a small room or cupboard: "My *closet* is big enough to hold all my toys."

302

clothed (klō*th*d) dressed in: "He was *clothed* in rags."

clothes (klōz *or* klō*th*z) something to wear on the body: "We put on our *clothes*."

coach (kōch) **1.** a railroad car with seats for passengers: "We rode in the *coach*." **2.** a person who teaches, trains, or tutors other people in areas such as sports, acting, school, or music.

col·lect·ed (kə lek'tid) gathered in one place: "My dad *collected* stamps."

com·put·er (kəm pyo͞ot'ər) an electronic device used to select and store information: "Some libraries keep track of their books by *computer*."

cos·tume (kos'to͞om *or* kos'tyo͞om) clothing worn by someone dressing as someone else: "The *costume* was very colorful."

cov·ered (kuv'ərd) placed one thing over another: "The mother *covered* the sick child with a blanket."

cov·ers (kuv'ərz) anything placed over another thing, such as blankets or lids: "Put the *covers* on the jars."

cra·zy (kra'zē) **1.** very foolish **2.** very eager or enthusiastic: "I am *crazy* about horses."

a fat	oi oil	ch chin
ā ape	o͝o look	sh she
ä car, father	o͞o tool	th thin
e ten	ou out	*th* then
er care	u up	zh leisure
ē even	ur fur	n͡g ring
i hit		
ir here	ə = a *in* ago	
ī bite, fire	e *in* agent	
o lot	i *in* unity	
ō go	o *in* collect	
ô law, horn	u *in* focus	

coach

D

danc·ing (dans'in͡g) moving the body and feet in a kind of rhythm, usually to music: "The children had fun in their *dancing* class."

de·cid·ed (di sīd'id) chosen after thought: "We *decided* to play ball."

de·li·cious (di lish'əs) very pleasing to the taste or smell: "The meal was *delicious*."

dancing

dollar

dragon

duckling

die (dī) stop living: "The plant will *die* without water."

dif·fer·ent (dif'ər ənt *or* dif'rənt) not alike; not the same: "I am *different* from my sister."

dis·cov·er·y (dis kuv'ər ē) finding, learning, or seeing something for the first time: "The *discovery* of the wheel helped people do work."

dol·lars (dol'ərz) United States coins or paper money; one dollar is equal to 100 cents: "It costs five *dollars*."

done (dun) **1.** worked or carried out an action. **2.** finished: "My homework is *done*."

drag·ons (drag'ənz) make-believe monsters that look like big lizards and breathe fire and smoke: "The *dragons* in the story scared me."

drew (droo) made a picture with pen, pencil, or crayon: "He *drew* a picture of birds flying."

duck·ling (duk'ling) a young duck: "The *duckling* stayed close to its mother."

dur·ing (door'ing *or* dyoor'ing) at some time in: "I go to camp *during* the summer."

E

ear·ly (ur'lē) near the beginning: "The bus came *early* in the morning."

earth (urth) **1.** the planet we live on. **2.** the ground or soil: "I dug for worms in the *earth*."

ea·si·ly (ē'z'l ē) without trying too hard: "Our team is *easily* the best."

en·gine (en'jən) **1.** a machine that uses energy to move or do work. **2.** the first car of a train: "The *engine* pulled the train up the hill."

en·joy (in joi′) get great pleasure from: "I *enjoy* reading mystery stories."

en·ter (en′tər) come or go in or into: "Please *enter* by the front door."

er·rands (er′əndz) short trips to do something: "I'm doing *errands* for my parents."

e·ven (ē′vən) **1.** flat; smooth. **2.** though it may seem unlikely: "*Even* a baby can do that."

ex·cuse (ik skyo͞oz′) **1.** reason or explanation. **2.** allow to go: "*Excuse* me. May I leave the room?"

ex·hib·its (ig zib′its) something shown or displayed: "The *exhibits* at the science museum were very interesting."

ex·pect (ik spekt′) to think something will happen: "I *expect* you to be on time."

a fat	**oi** oil	**ch** chin
ā ape	**o͞o** look	**sh** she
ä car, father	**o͞o** tool	**th** thin
e ten	**ou** out	***th*** then
er care	**u** up	**zh** leisure
ē even	**ur** fur	**n̂g** ring
i hit		
ir here	ə = a *in* ago	
ī bite, fire	e *in* agent	
o lot	i *in* unity	
ō go	o *in* collect	
ô law, horn	u *in* focus	

F

fa·mous (fā′məs) very well known: "The baseball player was *famous*."

feath·ers (fe*th*′ərz) soft, light parts covering the body of a bird: "The bird lost its *feathers*."

few (fyo͞o) not many: "*Few* people believed his story."

fight (fīt) **1.** battle; struggle: "The boys *fight* over who goes first." **2.** work hard to try to overcome.

fin·ished (fin′isht) came to an end: "I *finished* my homework."

floor (flôr) the flat bottom part of a room on which to walk: "My wet shoes squeaked as I walked across the *floor*."

flow·ers (flou′ərz) usually, brightly colored parts of plants that bear the seeds: "The *flowers* were beautiful."

feather

flowers

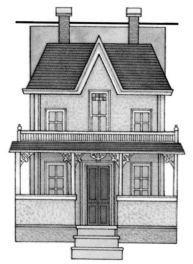

front

gas station

grinding stone

fol·lowed (fol′ōd) came after: "My sister went to school first, and I *followed* her."

for·est (fôr′ist) many trees growing closely together: "The *forest* was full of oak trees and pine trees."

front (frunt) the part that faces forward: "The *front* of the house was painted white."

frost (frôst) frozen water in the form of white crystals: "The grass was covered with *frost*."

G

gal·ler·y (gal′ə rē) a room or a place for showing works of art: "The paintings were on display in the *gallery*."

gar·lic (gär′lik) a plant like an onion whose bulb is used as a seasoning: "*Garlic* has a strong smell."

gas sta·tion (gas′ stā′shən) a place where gasoline and oil are sold and where cars are repaired: "Our car was fixed at the *gas station*."

gi·ant (jī′ənt) very great in size: "The *giant* plant was as large as a tree."

gi·ants (jī′əntz) make-believe beings that look like people but are much bigger and stronger: "The *giants* in the story could move a house."

glide (glīd) move along smoothly and easily: "We watched the skater *glide* along the ice."

grew (gro͞o) **1.** became larger or taller. **2.** became: "I *grew* tired by the end of the day."

grind·ing stone (grīnd′ing stōn) a flat, rounded stone used to crush foods: "The woman used a *grinding stone* to grind the corn into cornmeal."

groaned (grōnd) made a deep sound caused by sorrow or pain: "We *groaned* when the teacher gave us homework."

guess (ges) think or suppose: "I *guess* you are correct."

gut·ter (gut'ər) a narrow channel or groove: "The *gutter* on the roof filled with rain."

gym (jim) a building or room for exercises or playing games: "We ran in the *gym*."

a fat	oi oil	ch chin
ā ape	oo look	sh she
ä car, father	o͞o tool	th thin
e ten	ou out	*th* then
er care	u up	zh leisure
ē even	ur fur	n̑g ring
i hit		
ir here	ə = a *in* ago	
ī bite, fire	e *in* agent	
o lot	i *in* unity	
ō go	o *in* collect	
ô law, horn	u *in* focus	

H

han·di·caps (han'dē kaps) conditions that make some things harder to do: "Our school has a ramp at the front door for people who have physical *handicaps*."

hap·pened (hap"nd) occurred; took place: "The crash *happened* yesterday."

hap·pi·est (hap'ē ist) feeling or showing the greatest joy or pleasure: "It was my *happiest* birthday."

gutter

hawk (hôk) a large bird that eats smaller birds and other animals: "A *hawk* has very sharp eyesight."

heart (härt) **1.** a muscle that pumps blood through the body. **2.** the center. **3.** the human heart, thought of as something with feelings such as love, kindness, and sadness: "He gave to others because he had a kind *heart*."

heav·y (hev'ē) hard to lift or move because it weighs a lot: "The piano was *heavy*."

held (held) **1.** taken and kept in hands or arms. **2.** kept in a certain place: "She *held* her hand over her mouth." **3.** saved for later use.

heavy

her·self (hər self') **1.** her own self: "She hurt *herself*." **2.** her usual self.

high·er (hī'ər) above: "If I stand on this ladder, I will be *higher* than you."

his·to·ry (his'tə rē) what has happened in the past: "The *history* of the club was written by Eric."

howdy

hurt

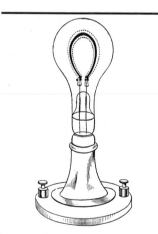

invention

hol·low (hol′ō) having an empty space on the inside: "The wall was *hollow*."

hoo·ray (hoo rā′) a word called out to show joy: "*Hooray*, it's time for vacation."

hours (ourz) **1.** more than one time segment equal to sixty minutes. **2.** the time it takes to do something: "It took *hours* to get there."

how·dy (hou′dē) hello: "She said *howdy* when we met."

hurt (hurt) cause pain or injury to: "I *hurt* my finger when I cut it."

I

i·de·a (ī dē′ə) a belief or a thought: "Jim's *idea* solved the problem."

i·mag·ine (i maj′in) form a picture in one's mind; think; suppose: "I like to *imagine* that I can fly."

im·por·tant (im pôr′t′nt) having much meaning or value: "Peggy's basketball game was *important*."

in·for·ma·tion (in′fər mā′shən) something told or facts learned: "We found the *information* we needed in the library."

in·stead (in sted′) in place of the other: "I snack on carrots *instead* of candy."

in·ter·est·ing (in′trist ing *or* in′tər ist ing) stirring up a feeling of wanting to know, learn, or see something: "The game looks *interesting* to me, and I would like to learn how to play."

in·ven·tions (in ven′shənz) things made that did not exist before: "Many *inventions* help make life easier."

308

J

jew·els (jōō′əlz) precious stones: "The ring was made of *jewels*."

join (join) take part along with others: "Please *join* us for dinner."

joined (joind) connected together: "The islands were *joined* by a bridge."

jour·ney (jur′nē) a trip: "It was a fast *journey* by airplane."

joy (joi) **1.** a happy feeling: "Watching him in the class play brought *joy* to his parents." **2.** anything that causes this feeling.

a fat	oi oil	ch chin
ā ape	oo look	sh she
ä car, father	ōō tool	th thin
e ten	ou out	*th* then
er care	u up	zh leisure
ē even	ur fur	ñg ring
i hit		
ir here	ə = a *in* ago	
ī bite, fire	e *in* agent	
o lot	i *in* unity	
ō go	o *in* collect	
ô law, horn	u *in* focus	

K

kneels (nēlz) rests on a knee or knees: "He *kneels* to dig in the sand."

knife (nīf) a tool with a flat, sharp blade: "Give each person a *knife*, fork, and spoon."

kneels

L

lad·der (lad′ər) a frame for climbing up or down: "We climbed the *ladder* to reach the roof."

large (lärj) of great size: "The box was so *large* I hid behind it."

la·ter (lā′tər) after some time: "I will eat dinner *later*."

ladders

lighthouse

lights

Lat·in (lat″n) the language of ancient Romans: "Long ago many people spoke *Latin*."

les·son (les″n) something to be learned, as by a student: "I have a piano *lesson* this afternoon."

li·ber (lī′bər) Latin word meaning book: "The word 'library' comes from *liber*."

li·brar·i·ans (lī brer′ē ənz) persons in charge of a library: "The *librarians* showed us how to use the card catalog."

li·brar·y (lī′brer′ē) a place where collections of books are kept for reading or borrowing: "A *library* is a good place to get information about many things." **libraries.**

light·house (līt′hɑus) a tower with a bright light on top to guide ships at night or in fog: "We could see the flashing light on the *lighthouse*."

lights (līts) sources of light such as lamps: "Turn on the *lights* when it gets dark."

lone·some (lōn′səm) **1.** alone. **2.** having a lonely feeling: "Everyone went out, and I was *lonesome*."

loud (lɑud) **1.** not quiet: "A *loud* noise woke me." **2.** noisy.

love·ly (luv′lē) beautiful; pleasing in looks or character: "The garden was *lovely* when the flowers bloomed."

M

mag·ic (maj′ik) a mysterious force or power: "It seemed that the car moved by *magic*."

mar·ried (mar′ēd) to be joined as husband and wife: "She *married* the man who lived next door."

mat·ter (mat'ər) **1.** what things are made of. **2.** to be of importance: "Your excuse does not *matter* to me."

meas·ured (mezh'ərd) set or marked off according to a standard or directions: "She *measured* the sugar before she added it."

med·i·cine (med'ə s'n) something used to cure disease or improve health: "The *medicine* helped me feel better."

might (mīt) to be possible or likely: "It *might* rain in the afternoon."

min·ers (mī'nərz) people who dig ore in mines: "The *miners* worked very hard to dig gold out of the mine."

moc·ca·sins (mok'ə s'nz) shoes or slippers made of soft leather: "*Moccasins* are soft leather shoes."

mon·ey (mun'ē) coins or paper bills used to buy and sell things: "I'm saving the *money* I earn from doing chores to buy a new soccer ball."

moun·tain (moun't'n) a very high hill: "We walked to the top of the *mountain*."

mouth (mouth) the opening on the face that people use for talking or eating: "I opened my *mouth* wide so the dentist could look at my teeth."

mu·se·um (myo͞o zē'əm) a building or room for keeping and showing things that are important or interesting: "The *museum* had dinosaur skeletons."

mu·sic (myo͞o'zik) sounds put together for singing or playing an instrument: "I like to listen to *music*."

a fat	oi oil	ch chin
ā ape	o͝o look	sh she
ä car, father	o͞o tool	th thin
e ten	ou out	*th* then
er care	u up	zh leisure
ē even	ur fur	n̈g ring
i hit		
ir here	ə = a *in* ago	
ī bite, fire	e *in* agent	
o lot	i *in* unity	
ō go	o *in* collect	
ô law, horn	u *in* focus	

measured

moccasins

N

nickel

neighs (nāz) whinnies; makes sounds like those of a horse: "The horse *neighs* and wakes me up."

nick·el (nik″l) **1.** a silver-white metal. **2.** a unit of money equal to five cents: "The school newspaper costs one *nickel*."

noise (noiz) a sound, especially a loud, unpleasant sound: "We made too much *noise*."

none (nun) not one; not any: "*None* of the shoes fit."

noon (nōon) twelve o'clock in the daytime: "We eat lunch at *noon*."

noth·ing (nuth'ing) not anything: "There is *nothing* I need at the store today."

No·vem·ber (nō vem′bər) the eleventh month of the year: "*November* is the month after October."

O

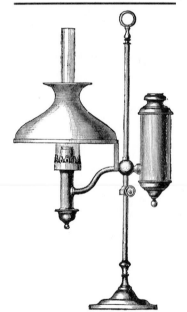

oil lamp

oil (oil) any of several greasy liquids that come from animals, vegetables, or minerals such as whale oil, peanut oil, or petroleum: "*Oil* can be burned to light special lamps."

or·gan·ized (ôr′gə nīzd) arranged according to a system: "My baseball cards are *organized* according to team."

P

a fat	oi oil	ch chin
ā ape	oo look	sh she
ä car, father	o͞o tool	th thin
e ten	ou out	*th* then
er care	u up	zh leisure
ē even	ur fur	n̄g ring
i hit		
ir here	ə = a *in* ago	
ī bite, fire	e *in* agent	
o lot	i *in* unity	
ō go	o *in* collect	
ô law, horn	u *in* focus	

par·cels (pär′s′lz) small, wrapped packages; bundles: "Maria came home from shopping with many *parcels*."

par·ents (per′ənts) father and mother: "I love my *parents*."

park (pärk) **1.** a place with trees, grass, and benches where people come to rest or play: "We play ball in the *park*." **2.** to leave a car or other vehicle in a certain place for a time.

pas de chat (pä′ də shä′) French word for a kind of ballet step: "The dance teacher taught us to do a *pas de chat*."

peace (pēs) **1.** freedom from war or fighting. **2.** calm or quiet: "They were at *peace*."

pep·per (pep′ər) **1.** a plant eaten as a vegetable. **2.** a seasoning made from the berries of a plant: "I added salt and *pepper* to the meat."

pi·an·o (pē an′ō) a large musical instrument with a keyboard: "We listened to Sara play beautiful music on the *piano*."

piece (pēs) a part of a whole thing: "A *piece* of the puzzle was lost."

pine cone (pīn kōn) fruit of a pine tree, holding seeds: "The squirrel ate the seeds inside the *pine cone*."

pi·o·neers (pī′ə nirz′) people who go first, making the way easier for those who follow: "The life of the *pioneers* was very hard."

plas·tered (plas′tərd) covered with a mixture used for coating walls or ceilings: "She *plastered* the wall."

park

pas de chat

313

points

proud

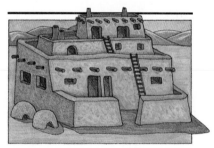

pueblo

play·er (plā′ər) a person who plays a game or musical instrument: "Each *player* on the team works with the others."

pla·za (plä′zə *or* plaz′ə) a public area or square: "They danced in the *plaza*."

points (points) **1.** sharp ends. **2.** aim a finger to: "He *points* at what he wants."

prac·tice (prak′tis) do something over and over in order to become skilled at it: "Each time I visit the library, I *practice* using the card catalog."

prob·lem (prob′ləm) something difficult to deal with or hard to understand: "I talked over my *problem* with my father, and he helped me to solve it."

pro·tect·ed (prə tek′təd) guarded or defended against harm or danger: "The gloves *protected* our hands from the cold."

proud (proud) **1.** think well of oneself. **2.** feeling pride or pleasure: "Father was *proud* of my good work."

pub·lic (pub′lik) for the use or good of everyone: "You can borrow books at no cost from the *public* library."

pueb·lo (pweb′lō) Spanish word for village or people who live in the villages: "The homes in the *pueblo* are built of stone or adobe bricks."

Q

quar·ter (kwôr′tər) **1.** one of four equal parts of something. **2.** a unit of money equal to twenty-five cents: "Each cup of lemonade cost a *quarter*."

ques·tions (kwes′chənz) things asked in order to learn or know: "The children asked the teacher *questions* about the new spelling words."

qui·et (kwī′ət) **1.** not noisy: "We must be *quiet* in the library so people can work." **2.** still; not moving.

a fat	oi oil	ch chin
ā ape	oo look	sh she
ä car, father	ōo tool	th thin
e ten	ou out	*th* then
er care	u up	zh leisure
ē even	ur fur	nĝ ring
i hit		
ir here	ə = a *in* ago	
ī bite, fire	e *in* agent	
o lot	i *in* unity	
ō go	o *in* collect	
ô law, horn	u *in* focus	

R

re·cess (rē′ses *or* ri ses′) **1.** a hidden or hollow place in a surface. **2.** a stopping of work or study: "We played ball during *recess*."

re·cord play·er (rek′ərd plā′ər) **1.** a machine used to play the sound signals placed on phonograph records. "We listened to our new records on the *record player*."

res·cue (res′kyoo) free or save from danger or evil: "The fire fighters came to *rescue* the people from the fire."

re·turned (ri turnd′) came back to a place: "After school, I *returned* home."

roof (roof *or* roof) the outside top covering of a building: "She fixed the *roof* so the rain will not come in."

roots (roots) the parts of a plant that grow in the ground: "The *roots* held the plant in the ground."

rescue

S

sack (sak) a bag made of coarse cloth: "The *sack* was filled with toys."

salt (sôlt) a white substance made of crystals used to flavor food: "*Salt* on the food made me thirsty."

Sat·ur·day (sat′ər dē) the seventh day of the week: "The day after Friday is *Saturday*."

roots

sculpture

shelf

skate

sci·ence (sī′əns) knowledge from facts learned from study and observation: "*Science* helps us understand how and why things happen."

screamed (skrēmd) made a loud, sharp cry: "The children *screamed* because they were hurt."

scrolls (skrōlz) rolls of paper with writing: "Long ago, things were written on *scrolls*."

sculp·tures (skulp′chərz) figures carved from wood or stone, or made from modeling clay: "The room was filled with *sculptures* of horses."

se·cret (sē′krit) something hidden or not known: "Tony did not tell anyone his *secret*."

se·quoi·a (si kwoi′ə) a large evergreen tree: "The *sequoia* tree was as high as a tall building."

se·ven (sev″n) one more than six: "I have *seven* dolls."

sewed (sōd) fastened with stitches made by a needle and thread: "Grandma *sewed* the pieces together."

shad·ow (shad′ ō) dark shape cast by light on an object: "I saw my *shadow* on the wall."

shak·ing (shāk′iṅg) **1.** moving quickly up and down, back and forth, or from side to side. **2.** trembling: "Ann was so cold she was *shaking*."

shelves (shelvz) thin, flat lengths of wood or metal fastened to a wall or frame and used to hold things: "The books were on the *shelves*."

shout·ed (shou′tid) said or called out loudly: "Mom *shouted* for me to come home."

sighed (sīd) took in and let out a long, deep breath: "He heard the news and *sighed*."

sim·ple (sim′p'l) easy to do: "The spelling test was *simple* for me because I knew all the words."

skate (skāt) glide or move along on ice: "She will *skate* across the pond."

skates (skāts) shoes with blades on them for gliding on ice: "Josh got new ice *skates* for his birthday."

slow·ly (slō′lē) **1.** not quickly. **2.** taking a long time: "Eric was late because he walked home *slowly*."

smooth·ly (smōō*th*′lē) moving evenly or gently: "The wagon rolled *smoothly* down the road."

sneak·ers (snē′kərz) shoes with rubber soles and heels worn for play and sports: "Howard wore his new *sneakers* to play outside."

soil (soil) **1.** the top layer of earth. **2.** the ground: "The *soil* was wet from the rain."

sold (sōld) gave in return for money: "I *sold* homemade bread to the people on my street."

space suits (spās′ sōōtz) special clothing worn in flights through outer space: "The astronauts wore *space suits* on their spaceflight."

spa·ghet·ti (spə get′ē) long, thin strings of food made from a paste of flour and water, cooked by boiling, and served with a sauce: "We ate *spaghetti* for dinner."

spe·cial (spesh′əl) important; different from others: "My dog Charlie is *special*."

split (split) **1.** separate into parts. **2.** a dance or acrobatic movement in which legs are spread in a straight line with one in front of the body and the other behind, or both legs out to the sides of the body: "It takes practice to learn to do a *split*."

spoiled (spoild) made worthless, useless, or rotten; ruined: "The meat was *spoiled,* so we put it in the garbage."

square (skwer) **1.** a flat figure with four equal sides. **2.** a park area of city with streets on four sides: "The party was held in the town *square*."

stand (stand) **1.** be or get in an upright position. **2.** put up with: "He couldn't *stand* the pain."

stir (stur) a mixing, circular motion usually made with a spoon: "Mary used a spoon to give the soup a *stir*."

a fat	oi oil	ch chin
ā ape	oo look	sh she
ä car, father	ōō tool	th thin
e ten	ou out	th then
er care	u up	zh leisure
ē even	ur fur	ŋ ring
i hit		
ir here	ə = a *in* ago	
ī bite, fire	e *in* agent	
o lot	i *in* unity	
ō go	o *in* collect	
ô law, horn	u *in* focus	

sneakers

spaghetti

stretches

stump

swan

storm (stôrm) a strong wind with heavy rain or snow: "A tree fell in the *storm*."

strange (strānj) **1.** unusual. **2.** not familiar; not known, seen, or heard before: "She wore a *strange* costume to the party."

stretch·es (strech'əz) draws out or pulls to a bigger size: "He *stretches* his arms over his head."

stroked (strōkd) rubbed something gently: "The mother *stroked* her daughter's long hair."

stud·ied (stud'ēd) learned by reading or thinking: "He *studied* spelling today."

stump (stump) the part of a tree left in the ground after the main part has been cut or fallen down: "We sat on the tree *stump* to rest."

sud·den·ly (sud"n lē) happening or coming quickly and without warning: "The storm came up *suddenly*."

su·per·mar·ket (sσο'pər mär'kit) a large food store: "We can buy all kinds of food and supplies at the *supermarket*."

sup·pose (sə pōz') assume, believe, or think: "I *suppose* you are correct."

swan (swon) a large, graceful water bird with a long, thin, curving neck: "We watched the *swan* glide through the water."

T

taste (tāst) notice the flavor of something by putting it in the mouth: "The *taste* was sweet."

taught (tôt) helped to learn; showed how to do something: "He *taught* the dog tricks."

teas·ing (tēz'ing) bothering or annoying: "The mother found the children *teasing* the cat."

tel·e·phone (tel′ə fōn) an instrument for sending and receiving sounds over wires: "I answered the *telephone* when it rang."

ter·ri·ble (ter′ə b'l) **1.** causing fear. **2.** bad or unpleasant: "The traffic made the trip *terrible*."

them·selves (*th*em selvz′) their own selves: "The children made the decorations *themselves*."

those (*th*ōz) used to point out the ones just mentioned: "*Those* books are mine."

threw (thr$\overline{oo}$) sent through the air: "Yesterday he *threw* the rock into the water."

throw (thrō) send through the air: "Please *throw* the ball to me."

to·night (tə nīt′) on or during this night: "We are going to a party *tonight*."

touch (tu*ch*) put a hand or finger on something to feel it: "You can *touch* my new coat."

treas·ure (trezh′ər) money, jewels, or things of value stored away: "The boat sank with *treasure* on it."

trimmed (trimd) made neat by clipping or cutting: "She *trimmed* her hair."

a fat	oi oil	ch chin
ā ape	oo look	sh she
ä car, father	o͞o tool	th thin
e ten	ou out	*th* then
er care	u up	zh leisure
ē even	ur fur	nĝ ring
i hit		
ir here	ə = a *in* ago	
ī bite, fire	e *in* agent	
o lot	i *in* unity	
ō go	o *in* collect	
ô law, horn	u *in* focus	

telephone

u

ug·ly (ug′lē) not pleasant to look at: "The empty old house was *ugly*."

un·der·stand (un dər stand′) get the meaning of: "Do you *understand* my answer?"

u·su·al·ly (y$\overline{oo}$′zhoo wəl lē) commonly; ordinarily: "This is the way we *usually* do things."

touch

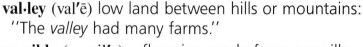

valley

val·ley (val′ē) low land between hills or mountains: "The *valley* had many farms."

va·nil·la (və nil′ə) a flavoring made from a vanilla bean: "We added *vanilla* to the cake batter."

W

wag·on (wag′ən) a vehicle with four wheels: "I pulled the *wagon* home."

washed (wôshd *or* woshd) **1.** cleaned with water. **2.** carried away with water: "The sand castle was *washed* away."

waves

waves (wāvz) the curving swells of water moving along the surface of an ocean: "The *waves* made the boat rock back and forth."

wheel·chair (hwēl′cher) a chair, on wheels, used by people who are handicapped, injured, or sick, to move from place to place: "He used the *wheelchair* to go from one room to another."

wheeled (hwēld) moved on wheels: "The librarian *wheeled* the slide projector in on a cart."

wher·ev·er (hwer ev′ər) in, at, or to a place: "We went *wherever* we were told to go."

which (hwich) that: "They picked apples *which* would make good pies."

whis·tling (hwis″ling) sounding like a whistle: "The *whistling* teakettle scared me."

wick (wik) the part of an oil lamp or candle that is lighted: "Hold the match to the *wick* to light the candle."

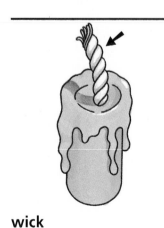

wick

wil·der·ness (wil′dər nis) a natural place unchanged by people: "The *wilderness* was more exciting than the city."

win·ter (win′tər) the season that follows fall; the coldest season: "In many places it snows in *winter*."

wom·en (wim′in) adult female persons: "The *women* played tennis."

won·der (wun′dər) **1.** a strange or unusual thing or event. **2.** wish to know: "I *wonder* why you called."

won·der·ful (wun′dər fəl) amazing; very good: "The box was filled with *wonderful* things."

wood·car·ver (wood′kär′vər) a person who cuts things out of wood: "We watched the *woodcarver* work at the craft fair."

wor·ried (wu′rēd) felt uneasy or anxious: "My parents *worried* when I did not come home on time."

wrote (rōt) **1.** formed words or letters. **2.** sent a message: "I *wrote* a letter to my pen pal."

a fat	oi oil	ch chin
ā ape	oo look	sh she
ä car, father	oo tool	th thin
e ten	ou out	th then
er care	u up	zh leisure
ē even	ur fur	ŋ ring
i hit		
ir here	ə = a *in* ago	
ī bite, fire	e *in* agent	
o lot	i *in* unity	
ō go	o *in* collect	
ô law, horn	u *in* focus	

woodcarver

Z

zoo (zoo) a place where wild animals are kept for the public to see: "Elephants are my favorite animals in the *zoo*."

zoo

321

The authors listed below have written some of the stories in this book. The information included in the notes was selected after asking pupils what they would like to know about authors.

ALIKI

ALIKI

Aliki's full name is Aliki Liacouras Brandenberg. She is a writer and an illustrator. Aliki's husband, Franz Brandenberg, is also a writer. She has drawn the pictures for all of her husband's books. She says about her writing, "I write two kinds of books—fiction (which comes from my own ideas) and nonfiction (which I must find out about from others)." Aliki grew up in New Jersey. She and her family now live in England. *(Born 1929)*

HANS CHRISTIAN ANDERSEN

HANS CHRISTIAN ANDERSEN

Hans Christian Andersen was born in Denmark. His father was a shoemaker, and his mother was a washerwoman. The family was very poor. When Hans was fourteen years old he could not read or write, but he wanted to learn. When he was seventeen, he began going to school. Later he graduated from the University of Copenhagen. He once said that he wanted his stories to be read by "both young and old." *(1805–1875)*

CAROLINE ARNOLD

CAROLINE ARNOLD

Caroline Arnold is a writer and an artist. She says that she began writing when her children were small. "I thought I would write stories for children and illustrate them myself. However, nearly all my books have been nonfiction and most of them have been illustrated by other people." *(Born 1944)*

CLYDE ROBERT BULLA

CLYDE ROBERT BULLA

Clyde Robert Bulla wanted to be a writer from the time he was young. He never had any formal training about how to be a writer, but he read lots of books. He says that when he started school he thought words were wonderful. "By writing them and putting them together, I could make them say whatever I wanted them to say. It was a kind of magic. Reading was a kind of magic, too." *(Born 1914)*

ANN NOLAN CLARK

ANN NOLAN CLARK

Ann Nolan Clark won the Newbery Medal for her book *Secret of the Andes*. She has also won other awards for her writing. The first books she wrote were about Native Americans. She taught in a one-room school for many years. Her students were Tesugue Pueblo children. All her books are based on real life. She writes about the people and places she has known. *(Born 1898)*

AILEEN FISHER

Aileen Fisher has written many poems and stories. She has won awards for her writing. Many of her poems and stories are about the country. She says, "I write for children for a very simple reason. I enjoy it. I usually write about nature for the same reason. My day is not complete unless I have a good walk on a mountain trail with a dog." *(Born 1906)*

AILEEN FISHER

GAIL GIBBONS

Gail Gibbons writes books. She also illustrates books. She has drawn pictures for all her own books and many books by other authors. The first book that she wrote and illustrated was *Willy and his Wheel Wagon.* She says she enjoys drawing pictures for her own books. *(Born 1944)*

GAIL GIBBONS

LEE BENNETT HOPKINS

LEE BENNETT HOPKINS

Lee Bennett Hopkins has talked with many writers and illustrators. He writes about his talks with these people. He also writes poems for young people. He says, "I love doing children's books. Each one is a new challenge, a new day, a new spring for me." Lee Bennett Hopkins also puts together anthologies, or collections, of other people's poems. He goes through thousands of poems and chooses the twenty that he thinks children will enjoy most. *(Born 1938)*

JOHANNA HURWITZ

JOHANNA HURWITZ

Johanna Hurwitz is a writer and illustrator of books for young people. She is also a children's librarian. She says, "My parents met in a bookstore, and there has never been a moment when books were not important in my life." Johanna Hurwitz writes many letters to friends and relatives. She says, "I am sure the letter writing that I do has been the best type of training for my book writing." *(Born 1937)*

PAT HUTCHINS

Pat Hutchins was born in England. She writes and illustrates books for young people. When she was growing up, she and her brothers and sisters loved to play in the woods. They took care of birds and animals that were hurt. "One bird, a young crow who had fallen from his nest, became a special pet. He stayed with us and refused to fly away. He was quite a well-known character in the village." *(Born 1942)*

PAT HUTCHINS

RACHEL ISADORA

Rachel Isadora writes and illustrates children's books. She has also been a ballet dancer since she was eleven years old. Her books have won many awards, including the Boston Globe–Horn Book Award. Rachel Isadora's husband also writes books for young people. She has illustrated some of her husband's books.

RACHEL ISADORA

JACK KENT

JACK KENT

Jack Kent wrote and illustrated children's books. He said that his reason for writing and illustrating children's books was "to make a living doing what I enjoy." He loved books. "To me," he said, "the world is a fascinating place, and my books are attempts at sharing my feelings of wonder and pleasure." *(1920–1985)*

JOE LASKER

JOE LASKER

Joe Lasker was born in New York City. He writes and illustrates books, but he says, "Painting is my first love." He has illustrated all the books he has written. He also illustrates books for other authors. He has won awards for many of his books. *(Born 1919)*

LEO LIONNI

Leo Lionni was born in Holland and moved to the United States in 1939. He says, "I believe that a good children's book should appeal to all people who have not completely lost their original joy and wonder of life. The fact is that I really don't make books for children at all. I make them for that part of us, of myself and of my friends, which has never changed, which is still a child." Leo Lionni illustrates the books he writes. *(Born 1910)*

LEO LIONNI

ARNOLD LOBEL

Arnold Lobel wrote and illustrated books for young people. His *Frog and Toad Are Friends* was a Caldecott Honor Book, and *Frog and Toad Together* was a Newbery Honor Book. Arnold Lobel said that he always enjoyed making books for children. One of the things he liked best was being able to change a character that was not acting the way Lobel thought it should act. *(1933–1987)*

ARNOLD LOBEL

WALTER DEAN MYERS

WALTER DEAN MYERS

Walter Dean Myers was born in West Virginia. He grew up in New York City's Harlem. He says he enjoys writing for young people. "I particularly enjoy writing about the city life I know best." He has received many awards for his writing, including the American Library Association's Best Books for Young Adults and the Coretta Scott King Award. *(Born 1937)*

JACK PRELUTSKY

JACK PRELUTSKY

Jack Prelutsky is a poet. A friend liked his drawings of imaginary animals and his funny verses. The friend wanted him to try to get them published. He did. Since then Jack Prelutsky has written many books of poetry. He says that all of his characters contain parts of people he knows and parts of himself. Some of his books have been chosen as Junior Literary Guild selections and American Library Association Notable Books. Jack Prelutsky is also a singer, an actor, and a translator.

MIRIAM SCHLEIN

Miriam Schlein has written many books and stories for children. Several of her books have been Junior Literary Guild selections. Her books have also been translated into foreign languages, including German and Danish. Some of Miriam Schlein's books have been published in Braille. *(Born 1926)*

MIRIAM SCHLEIN

LaVADA WEIR

LaVada Weir's last name rhymes with *here*. She writes stories and plays. She says, "I am still turning out stories between loads of laundry, meals, and ailing appliances. I find that perhaps the most rewarding aspect of this field is meeting with groups of children and talking to them about their writing."

LA VADA WEIR

AUTHOR INDEX

"Frog and Toad" excerpt adapted from "Dragons and Giants" by Arnold Lobel, from *Frog and Toad Together* written and illustrated by Arnold Lobel. Copyright © 1971 by Arnold Lobel. Reprinted by permission of the American publisher, Harper & Row, Publishers, Inc., and of the British publisher, William Heinemann Ltd.

Harlequin and the Gift of Many Colors story by Remy Charlip and Burton Supree, paintings by Remy Charlip, Copyright © 1973 by the authors. Play adaptation by José Rivera, Copyright © 1989 by Remy Charlip and Burton Supree. Used by permission of James K. Ross, Literary Agent for Remy Charlip and Burton Supree. All rights, including commercial performance, motion picture, recitation, radio or television broadcasting, public reading, and rights of translation into foreign languages, are strictly reserved. Productions may not be produced on cable television, videotaped, or otherwise reproduced or transmitted by any electronic or mechanical means, or by any storage and retrieval system, unless written permission and quotations for royalty fee are obtained from Remy Charlip, 60 East 7th Street, New York, NY 10003.

"Helping" from *Where the Sidewalk Ends* by Shel Silverstein. Copyright © 1974 by Evil Eye Music, Inc. Reprinted by permission of the American publisher, Harper & Row, Publishers, Inc., and of the British publishers, Jonathan Cape Ltd.

"Houses" from *Up the Windy Hill* by Aileen Fisher. Copyright © 1953, renewed 1981 by Aileen Fisher. Reprinted by permission of Aileen Fisher.

"The House That Nobody Wanted" from *Junk Day on Juniper Street and Other Easy-to-Read Stories*, by Lilian Moore, Pictures by Arnold Lobel. Copyright © 1969 by Lilian Moore. All rights reserved. Text and art reprinted by permission of Bantam Books, art by Scholastic Inc., and text by Marian Reiner for the author.

Howdy! by LaVada Weir. Copyright © 1972 by Steck-Vaughn Company, Austin, Texas. Adapted and reprinted by permission of LaVada Weir.

Keep the Lights Burning, Abbie by Peter and Connie Roop, pictures by Peter E. Hanson. Copyright © 1985 by Carolrhoda Books, Inc. Reprinted by permission of Lerner Publications Company, 241 First Avenue North, Minneapolis, Minnesota 55401.

"Lee Bennett Hopkins Interviews Aliki," © 1989 by Silver, Burdett & Ginn Inc.

Maggie and the Goodbye Gift written and illustrated by Jerome E. Milord and Sue E. Milord. Copyright © 1979 by Jerome E. Milord and Sue E. Milord. By permission of Lothrop, Lee & Shepard Books (A Division of William Morrow).

Max story and pictures by Rachel Isadora. Slightly adapted and reprinted by permission of Macmillan Publishing Company. Copyright © 1976 by Rachel Isadora.

"Museum" from *What I Did Last Summer* by Jack Prelutsky. Text copyright © 1984 by Jack Prelutsky. By permission of Greenwillow Books (A Division of William Morrow).

My House by Miriam Schlein. Copyright © 1971 by Miriam Schlein. Adapted and reprinted by permission of the author.

"My Pueblo Home" from *In My Mother's House* by Ann Nolan Clark. Copyright 1941, renewed © 1969 by Ann Nolan Clark. Reprinted by permission of Viking Penguin Inc.

Nick Joins In written and illustrated by Joe Lasker. Copyright © 1980 by Joe Lasker. Adapted and reprinted by permission of Albert Whitman & Company.

"Not So Wise As You Suppose" by Michael Patrick Hearn, © 1989 by Silver, Burdett & Ginn Inc.

"Pueblos of the Southwest" by Anna Westcott, © 1989 by Silver, Burdett & Ginn Inc.

"The Skating Lesson" by Johanna Hurwitz, © 1989 by Silver, Burdett & Ginn Inc.

"The Smithsonian Institution" by Walter Dean Myers, © 1989 by Silver, Burdett & Ginn Inc.

The Story of Johnny Appleseed written and illustrated by Aliki. Copyright © 1963 by Aliki. Adapted and used by permission of the publisher, Prentice-Hall, Inc., Englewood Cliffs, N. J.

"Thinking" from *At the Top of My Voice and Other Poems* by Felice Holman. Published by Charles Scribner's Sons. Text copyright © by Felice Holman. Reprinted by permission of Felice Holman Valen.

Too Many Babas written and illustrated by Carolyn Croll. Copyright © 1979 by Carolyn Croll. Adapted and reprinted by permission of Harper & Row, Publishers, Inc. Illustrations specially prepared for Silver, Burdett & Ginn Inc. by Carolyn Croll based on her original illustrations.

334

"The Train Set" slightly adapted from *The Best Train Set Ever* written and illustrated by Pat Hutchins. Copyright © 1978 by Pat Hutchins. By permission of the American publisher, Greenwillow Books (a division of William Morrow), and of the British publisher, The Bodley Head Ltd.

"The Ugly Duckling" by Hans Christian Andersen, retold by Karen-Amanda Toulon, © 1989 by Silver, Burdett & Ginn Inc.

COVER: Maryjane Begin
DESIGN: Design Five, NYC and Kirchoff/ Wohlberg in cooperation with Silver Burdett & Ginn

ILLUSTRATION: 4, Lucinda McQueen; 5, (l) Lucinda McQueen, (r) Mary Beth Schwark; 6, Helen Davie; 7, (l) Michael Cobb & Diane Delancy, (r) Joe Ewers; 8, (b) Aliki; 9, Satoshi Kitamura; 10, Remy Charlip; 11, (t) Leo Lionni, (b) Carolyn Croll; 14–20, Arnold Lobel; 21, Sharron O'Neil; 22–33, Lucinda McQueen; 34, (c) from *Arrow to the Sun* by Gerald McDermott, copyright © 1974 by Gerald McDermott, all rights reserved, reprinted by permission of Viking Penguin, Inc., (b) from *Where the Wild Things Are* by Maurice Sendak, copyright © 1963 by Maurice Sendak, used with permission; 35, (t) from *Ben's Trumpet* by Rachel Isadora, copyright © 1974 by Rachel Isadora Maiorano, reproduced with the permission of the publisher, Greenwillow Books, a division of William Morrow & Co., Inc., (br) from *Trains* by Donald Crews, copyright © 1978 by Donald Crews, reproduced with permission of the publisher, Greenwillow Books, a division of William Morrow & Co., Inc.; 36–40, Rachel Isadora; 41, Susan Lexa; 44–55, Mary Beth Schwark; 56–57, Etienne Delessert; 60–70, Peter E. Hanson; 72–79, Jack Kent; 80, Susan Jaekel; 86–90, Michael Cobb & Diane Delancy; 91, Laurie Marks; 94–100, Steven Schindler; 102–103, Giles Larouche; 104–113, Joe Ewers; 115–120, Helen Davie; 122– 128, Melinda May Sullivan; 129, Gretchen Will Mayo; 142–149, Arnold Lobel; 150–152, Sharron O'Neil; 156–167, Toby Gowing; 168–176, Pat Hutchins; 177, Sharron O'Neil; 178, Floyd Cooper; 181, Sharron O'Neil; 184–190, Aliki; 191, Sharron O'Neil; 192, (t) McGuffey Museum, Miami University, Oxford, Ohio; 193, from *McGuffey's First Eclectic Reader,* McGuffey Museum, Miami University, Oxford, Ohio; 205, Sharron O'Neil; 206–207, Satoshi Kitamura; 208–217, Sue and Jerry Milord; 224–233, Carolyn Croll; 234–235, Tom Leonard; 238–244, Gail Gibbons; 245, Christa Kieffer; 246–252, Joe Lasker; 256–265, Jean Helmer; 266–280, Remy Charlip; 281, Susan Lexa; 284–293, Leo Lionni; 299, Melinda Fabian, Deirdre Griffin; 300, Diane Dawson Hearn; 301, Susan David, Melinda Fabian; 302, Melinda Fabian; 303, Roberta Holmes, Claudia Sargent; 304, Diane Dawson Hearn; 305, Melinda Fabian; 306, Claudia Sargent; 307, Diane Dawson Hearn, Claudia Sargent; 308, Diane Dawson Hearn, Roberta Holmes; 311, Roberta Holmes, Claudia Sargent; 313, Roberta Holmes; 314, Roberta Holmes, Claudia Sargent; 315, Deirdre Griffin, Roberta Holmes; 316, Roberta Holmes; 317, Claudia Sargent; 318, Susan David, Diane Dawson Hearn; 320, Deirdre Griffin.

PHOTOGRAPHY: 8, (t) National Museum of American Art, Smithsonian Institution; 12, *Girl with Roller Skates,* Abastenia St. Leger Eberle, bronze sculpture, Museum of Art, Rhode Island School of Design: gift of Mrs. Guestav Radeke; 34–35, (t) American Library Association; 35, (bl) Susan Hirschman, courtesy of Greenwillow Books, a division of William Morrow & Co., Inc.; 83, (t) from *Petunia,* written and illustrated by Roger Duvoisin, copyright © 1950, reprinted with permission of Knopf, (c) from *The Mixed-Up Chameleon* by Eric Carle, copyright © 1984, reprinted with permission of Crowell, (b) from *Say Hello, Vanessa* by Marjorie Weinman Sharmat, illustrated by Lillian Hoban, copyright © 1979, reprinted with permission of Holiday House; 84, Shelburne Museum, Shelburne, Vermont, copyright © 1986, Grandma Moses Properties Co., New York; 114–115, Gerald Corsi, Tom Stack & Associates; 130, Craig Aurness/West Light; 132, Peter LeGrand/Click, Chicago; 134, (t) William R. Wright/Taurus Photos, (b) Joan Liftin/ Archive Pictures, Inc.; 135, (r) Eric Carle/Shostal Associates, (l) courtesy of Matchbox, Lesney Products, Inc.; 136, (t) David Woo/Stock, Boston, (b) Ann Hagen Griffiths/OPC; 137, (t) copyright © Joseph Nettis/Photo Researchers, (b) Walter Frerck/ Odyssey Productions; 138, Randy Brandon/ Aperture; 153, (tr) from *A House Is a House for Me* by Mary Ann Hoberman, jacket illustration by Betty Fraser, illustrations copyright © 1978 by Betty Fraser, all rights reserved, reprinted by permission of Viking Penguin, Inc., (tl) from *Evan's Corner* by Elizabeth Starr Hill, illustrated by Nancy Grossman, copyright © 1967, reprinted by permission of

335

Holt, Rinehart & Winston, (br) from *The Little House,* stories and pictures by Virginia Lee Burton, copyright © 1942, reprinted by permission of Houghton Mifflin, (bl) from *Always Room for One More* by Sorche Nic Leodhas, illustrated by Nonny Hogrogian, copyright © 1965, reprinted by permission of Holt, Rinehart & Winston; 154, "Flowering Plum and Orchid." After Yun Shou-p'ing (1663–1690), Chinese. Detail of a handscroll, *The Hundred Flowers,* ink and colors on silk, 18th century. L.1981.126.42, The Metropolitan Museum of Art, New York; 178, Ian Bradshaw; 192, (b) Carlos Vergara; 196, Bill Barley, Superstock; 198, (l) National Museum of American Art, Smithsonian Institution, (r) Photri, Inc.; 199–200, National Museum of American Art, Smithsonian Institution; 201, Kjell Sandved; 202, Pete Saloutos, The Stock Market; 203, (l) S.M. Highsmith, Uniphoto, (r) Alese & Mort Pechter, The Stock Market; 204, National Museum of American Art, Smithsonian Institution; 221, (tr) from *A Chair for My Mother* by Vera B. Williams, copyright © 1982, reprinted by permission of Greenwillow Books, a division of William Morrow & Co., Inc., (tl) from *The Giving Tree* by Shel Silverstein, copyright © 1964, reprinted by permission of Harper & Row, (br) from *The Best Present Is Me,* written and illustrated by Janet Wolf, copyright © 1984, reprinted by permission of Harper & Row, (bl) from *Mr. Rabbit and the Lovely Present* by Charlotte Zolotow, pictures by Maurice Sendak, copyright © 1962, reprinted by permission of Harper & Row; 222, Layton Art Collection, Milwaukee Art Museum; 235, John Lei/OPC; 256, Gene Ahrens/Bruce Coleman, Inc.; 297, (tr) from *Where Does the Teacher Live?* by Paula Kurzband Feder, illustrated by Lillian Hoban, illustrations copyright © 1979 by Lillian Hoban, reproduced by permission of the publisher, E.P. Dutton, a division of NAL Penguin, Inc., (tl) from *Brave Irene* by William Steig, copyright © 1986, reprinted by permission of Straus & Giroux, (br) from *Send Wendell* by Genevieve Gray, drawings by Symeon Shimin, copyright © 1974, reprinted by permission of McGraw-Hill, (bl) from *The 100-Year-Old Cactus* by Anita Holmes, illustrated by Carol Lerner, illustrations copyright © 1983 by Carol Lerner, reproduced with permission of Four Winds Press, and Imprint of Macmillan Publishing Company; 299, Donald Dietz/Stock Boston; 300, Bettmann Archive, copyright © Frank Siteman 1988; 302, copyright © Frank Siteman 1988; 304, copyright © Frank Siteman 1988, Laura Riley/Bruce Coleman, Inc.; 305, John Urban; 306, Donald Dietz/Stock Boston, Tom Pantages; 308, North Wind Archive; 309, copyright © Frank Siteman 1988, Stephen G. Maka; 310, copyright © Frank Siteman 1988; 312, copyright © Frank Siteman 1988, North Wind Archive; 313, Stephen G. Maka; 316, copyright © Frank Siteman 1988, David F. Hughes/Stock Boston; 318, Stephen G. Maka; 319, copyright © Frank Siteman 1988; 320, Stephen G. Maka, Sera Hopkins; 321, Tom Pantages, Ruth Lacey; 323, (t) Bettmann Archive; 324, (b) Viking Penguin, Inc.; 325, (t) Bettmann Archive, (b) Harper & Row; 326, (t) provided by author, (b) Viking Penguin, Inc.; 327, (t) Harper & Row, (b) Jack Kendrick; 328, (b) provided by author; 329, (t) provided by author; 331, provided by author.

E F G H I J—RRD—96 95 94 93 92 91 90 89